Practice Tests

for

Peoples and Bailey's

HUMANITY

An Introduction to Cultural Anthropology

Sixth Edition

James Peoples
Ohio Wesleyan University

Garrick Bailey
University of Tulsa

Bruce P. Wheatley
University of Alabama, Birmingham

THOMSON

WADSWORTH

Australia • Canada • Mexico • Singapore • Spain • United Kingdom • United States

Printed in the United States of America
1 2 3 4 5 6 7 07 06 05 04 03

Printer: West

0-534-58846-8

For more information about our products, contact us at:
Thomson Learning Academic Resource Center
1-800-423-0563

For permission to use material from this text, contact us by:
Phone: 1-800-730-2214
Fax: 1-800-730-2215
Web: http://www.thomsonrights.com

Wadsworth/Thomson Learning
10 Davis Drive
Belmont, CA 94002-3098
USA

Asia
Thomson Learning
5 Shenton Way #01-01
UIC Building
Singapore 068808

Australia/New Zealand
Thomson Learning
102 Dodds Street
Southbank, Victoria 3006
Australia

Canada
Nelson
1120 Birchmount Road
Toronto, Ontario M1K 5G4
Canada

Europe/Middle East/South Africa
Thomson Learning
High Holborn House
50/51 Bedford Row
London WC1R 4LR
United Kingdom

Latin America
Thomson Learning
Seneca, 53
Colonia Polanco
11560 Mexico D.F.
Mexico

Spain/Portugal
Paraninfo
Calle/Magallanes, 25
28015 Madrid, Spain

Table of Contents

Preface

Dear Student,

Welcome to the Practice Tests for Peoples and Bailey's *Humanity: An Introduction to Cultural Anthropology,* Sixth Edition. The goal of this booklet is to help you test and apply your knowledge of chapter concepts as you read the textbook and prepare for examinations. To be most effective, read and study the textbook before using the tests. After reading a chapter, use the practice tests to identify concepts that you may need to review more carefully.

This set to practice tests includes multiple-choice questions and true-false statements for each chapter in the textbook. The correct answers are listed at the end of each chapter along with a page reference to the textbook.

Good luck, and enjoy the study of cultural anthropology!

Sincerely,

James Peoples   **Garrick Bailey**   **Bruce P. Wheatley**
Ohio Wesleyan University   *University of Tulsa*   *University of Alabama–Birmingham*

Chapter 1

THE STUDY OF HUMANITY

Multiple Choice Questions

1. Which of the following are the five major subfields of anthropology?

   A. archaeology, anthropological linguistics, cultural anthropology, ethnology, primatology
   B. anthropological linguistics, physical anthropology, archaeology, applied anthropology, cultural anthropology
   C. physical anthropology, prehistoric archaeology, primatology, ethnography, linguistics
   D. archaeology, paleoanthropology, ethnology, forensic anthropology, applied anthropology

2. Medical, corporate, and educational anthropology are part of which major subfield?

   A. physical anthropology
   B. anthropological linguistics
   C. cultural anthropology
   D. applied anthropology

3. Which of the following is not one of the major subfields of anthropology?

   A. anthropological linguistics
   B. forensic anthropology
   C. archaeology
   D. physical anthropology
   E. applied anthropology

4. An anthropologist who studies subjects such as the origins of agriculture and the earliest civilizations is most likely to be"

   A. a cultural anthropologist
   B. an ethnologist
   C. a physical anthropologist
   D. an archaeologist

5. Primatologists study:

   A. our fossil ancestors
   B. plant pollen
   C. monkeys and apes
   D. prehistoric people and their sites

6. The study of ancient cultures is the job of:

    A. historic anthropology
    B. ethnology
    C. prehistoric archaeology
    D. educational anthropology

7. Jane Goodall is famous for her pioneering work in:

    A. paleoanthropology
    B. primatology
    C. contract archaeology
    D. forensic anthropology

8. An anthropologist who studies human biological evolution is a:

    A. primatologist
    B. historic archaeologist
    C. ethnologist
    D. paleoanthropologist

9. The human lineage split from the ape lineage probably about:

    A. five million years ago
    B. one hundred thousand years ago
    C. five thousand years ago
    D. one million years ago

10. The excavation of material remains from the remote past is a task for what subfield of anthropology?

    A. cultural
    B. physical
    C. archaeology
    D. linguistics

11. A written account or description of a particular culture is called:

    A. an ethnology
    B. a novel
    C. an ethnography
    D. enculturation

12. Anthropologists who move into a community under study, communicate with people in the local language, and interact daily with members of a community are referred to as:

   A. fieldworkers
   B. anthropologists
   C. linguists
   D. field researchers

13. Linguists:

   A. describe and analyze the structures of human languages
   B. conduct fieldwork in many different cultures of the world
   C. study fossil humans
   D. survey and excavate archaeological sites

14. The anthropological subfield that studies human language is called:

   A. historic archaeology
   B. linguistics
   C. forensics
   D. ethology

15. Applied anthropologists work in:

   A. development anthropology
   B. educational anthropology
   C. medical anthropology
   D. all of the above

16. The process by which different peoples of the world affect each other is called:

   A. ethnocentrisim
   B. applied anthropology
   C. holism
   D. globalization

17. Anthropologists who advise in bilingual education and observe classroom interactions are called:

   A. prehistoric archaeologists
   B. development anthropologists
   C. educational anthropologists
   D. paleoanthropologists

18. One important factor separating cultural anthropology from other disciplines that study humanity is:

A. anthropologists only go to "exotic" places
B. fieldwork
C. the ethnocentrism of ethnographers
D. anthropologists tend to ignore religion and art in understanding other cultures

19. If you temporarily suspend the moral standards and assumptions of your own culture in order to better understand another culture, you are taking the _____ perspective.

A. relativistic
B. holistic
C. comparative
D. integrative

20. General statements about human beings are likely to be erroneous unless a wide range of cultures is studied. This is the _____ perspective of anthropology.

A. scientific
B. comparative
C. biological
D. relativistic

21. The belief that one's own cultural values are superior to those of another culture is called:

A. ethnocentrism
B. cultural relativism
C. cultural resource management
D. comparativism

22. The belief that no culture is superior or inferior to any other culture is called:

A. ethnocentrism
B. cultural relativism
C. cultural resource management
D. comparativism

23. Cultural anthropology's holistic perspective is described best by which phrase?

A. understanding without morally judging
B. analyzing through comparison
C. explaining through controlled experimentation
D. understanding in context

24. Anthropologists generally agree that:

    A. there are only three general categories of races
    B. classifying people into discrete races is a cultural construct
    C. the word "race" should not be eliminated from the 2010 American census
    D. genetic variation between races is much greater than genetic variation among individuals within a race

25. The idea of race as a cultural construct rather than a biological reality is supported by:

    A. genetic studies that show genetic variation within a given race exceeds the variation between races
    B. racial classification based on blood groups would yield a different classification than one based on skin color
    C. different cultures disagree on the number and definition of races
    D. all of the above

True / False Questions

1. Almost all anthropologists specialize in only one of five subfields.

2. Anthropology and its "sister discipline" of sociology are less distinctive today than a few decades ago.

3. Some physical anthropologists identify human skeletal remains.

4. Prehistoric archaeologists study human physical variation.

5. Ethnography means "writing about a people."

6. The American Anthropological Association recently voted to delete the subfield of applied anthropology.

7. The study of the way people attach labels to their environment and their perception of it is of interest to anthropologists in the subfield of linguistics.

8. Anthropologists only study "natives" in exotic lands.

9. More than any other single factor, the fieldwork experience distinguishes cultural anthropology from other disciplines concerned with humankind.

10. Cultural anthropologists regularly study subjects that are the specializations of other disciplines.

11. The holistic perspective means no culture is inherently superior or inferior to any other.

12. The comparative perspective takes only certain aspects of cultural diversity into account when generalizing about humans.

13. A relativistic outlook on cultural differences might help alleviate some of the misunderstandings between different peoples.

14. Most anthropologists today are moral relativists.

15. One of the values of anthropology is that it teaches us about the biological, technological, and cultural development of humanity over long time spans.

16. The modern meaning of culture, as used in the phrase "Japanese culture", is not very old.

17. According to cultural anthropologists, physical differences between human populations cannot explain differences in behavior or intelligence between groups of people.

18. Although physical differences between groups are influenced by genetics, the way Americans define "race" is culturally constructed.

19. Individuals within a racial category are much more diverse genetically than individuals belonging to different races.

20. Biological groups of people that can be objectively defined are known as races.

Multiple Choice Answers

1.	B	(p. 2)		14.	B	(p. 6)
2.	C	(p. 2)		15.	D	(p. 6)|
3.	B	(p. 2)		16.	D	(p. 8)
4.	D	(p. 4)		17.	C	(p. 7)
5.	C	(p. 2-3)		18.	B	(p. 9)
6.	C	(p. 4)		19.	A	(p. 10)
7.	B	(p. 3)		20.	B	(p. 10)
8.	D	(p. 3)		21.	A	(p. 10)
9.	A	(p. 3)		22.	B	(p. 10)
10.	C	(p. 5)		23.	D	(p. 10)
11.	C	(p. 5)		24.	B	(p. 14-15)
12.	A	(p. 6)		25.	D	(p. 14-15
13.	A	(p. 5)				

True / False Answers

1.	T	(p. 2)		11.	F	(p. 10)
2.	T	(p. 2)		12.	F	(p. 10)
3.	T	(p. 4)		13.	T	(p. 11)
4.	F	(p. 4)		14.	F	(p. 11)
5.	T	(p. 5)		15.	T	(p. 11)
6.	F	(p. 6)		16.	T	(p. 12)
7.	T	(p. 6)		17.	T	(p. 14)
8.	F	(p. 8)		18.	T	(p. 14)
9.	T	(p. 8)		19.	T	(p. 14)
10.	T	(p. 9)		20.	F	(p. 15)

Chapter 2

CULTURE

Multiple Choice Questions

1. Anthropologists say that culture is:

   A. learned
   B. shared
   C. largely responsible for group-level differences
   D. necessary to make individuals into complete persons
   E. all of the above

2. If one had to point to a so-called "missing link," it might be:

   A. *Australopithecus africanus*
   B. *Pan troglodytes*
   C. the gorilla
   D. *Homo sapiens*

3. The first change that began to differentiate the evolutionary line leading to modern apes from that leading to modern humans was:

   A. brain size
   B. tool use
   C. bipedalism
   D. all of the above

4. Which of these statements about human evolution is *true*?

   A. Scientists still have not discovered the "missing link."
   B. Of all primates, only humans make tools.
   C. Chimpanzees are our evolutionary ancestors.
   D. Paleoanthropologists today think the human family tree has multiple branches.

5. The first hominid known to have left Africa and found as far away from Africa as Indonesia and China was:

   A. *Australopithecus africanus*
   B. *Homo habilis*
   C. *Homo erectus*
   D. *Homo sapiens neanderthalensis*

6. Modern humans and modern apes:

   A. both belong to Hominidae
   B. share a common ancestor
   C. both evolved similar cranial capacities
   D. both had linear evolutionary trees

7. Cultures vary in their:

   A. biological/physical characteristics
   B. ways of thinking and behaving
   C. instincts
   D. trial-and-error learning

8. Cultural knowledge refers to:

   A. instincts
   B. biological characteristics
   C. attitudes, ideas, beliefs and other information stored in people's heads.
   D. All of the above

9. People who share a culture:

   A. are capable of communicating and interacting without needing to explain their behavior
   B. share a common cultural identity
   C. often live in the same society and share a common language and sense of identity
   D. all of the above

10. Social learning refers to learning by:

    A. enculturation
    B. trial-and-error
    C. instinct
    D. technological know-how

11. The most important aspect of cultural knowledge is:

    A. whether it is true
    B. whether it leads to behavior that is meaningful to others and adaptive to the natural and social environment.
    C. whether it is useful to a culture
    D. whether it is better or worse than another culture

12. The Semai:

    A. live in the Amazon rain forest
    B. are aggressive
    C. seldom express anger and hostility
    D. praise their children for their fierceness

13. The rights and duties an individual has with others in a group are called his or her:

    A. rank
    B. role
    C. status
    D. class

14. Norms are:

    A. followed by everyone in a culture all the time.
    B. often not very useful
    C. shared ideals about how people ought to act in certain situations
    D. provide the ultimate standards that people believe must be upheld in all circumstances

15. An example of how values provide us with cultural standards is:

    A. knowing how to act when entering a room full of strangers
    B. the idea that Chinese culture is better than Indian culture
    C. Bill of Rights in the Constitution
    D. that we learn such things through trial and error

16. Symbols allow us to:

    A. have a common understanding of the meanings of behaviors
    B. interact with one another without stating explicitly what we are doing and why
    C. interpret the meanings of behaviors based on a shared understanding
    D. all of the above

17. Two important properties of symbols are that their meanings are conventional and:

    A. iconic
    B. arbitrary
    C. religious
    D. always verbal or written

18. The Hanunoo are a people of the tropical forest in the Philippines. The fact that they identify and name more plants in their environment than would a scientific botanist shows that

    A. people of different cultures never agree on the "kinds" of things that exist.
    B. the Hanunoo are better observers of plants than are botanists
    C. either the Hanunoo or the botanist is mistaken, but we judge which because we are relativists.
    D. the Hanunoo and the botanists use different criteria in their classification of plants.

19. The personal zone of interpersonal spacing in Americans is:

    A. the same as all cultures
    B. farther than in other cultures such as Arabic and Iranian
    C. not important
    D. apparently a genetically learned behavior

20. A culture that classifies plants not only into various kinds, but also into various categories of usefulness:

   A. classifies reality different from us
   B. interprets a different world view
   C. differs from us in its values and symbols
   D. is ethnocentric

21. People who view themselves as masters of nature and other people who view themselves as living in harmony with nature differ in their:

   A. religion
   B. world view
   C. classification of reality and morality
   D. all of the above

22. A culture's classification of their kinship system is:

   A. "naturally" based, for example, mother
   B. biologically based
   C. part of its classification of reality
   D. the same everywhere, just interpreted differently

23. Which of the following is an example of a world view:

   A. expectations of behavior at a funeral
   B. the Bill of Rights to the Constitution
   C. the origin of good and evil
   D. meanings of nonverbal behavior

24. Culture is necessary for human existence because it:

   A. provides the skills needed to adapt to surroundings
   B. provides the basis for human social life
   C. provides the categories and beliefs through which people perceive the world around them.
   D. all of the above

25. The behavior of individuals in a culture varies and often departs from expectations because:

   A. no two people have the exact same life experiences, even though they were brought up in the same cultural setting.
   B. norms and values do not always provide clear guidelines for behavior.
   C. people must often choose between conflicting goals and values
   D. all of the above

26. Which of these statements about the relationship between "racial" differences and "cultural" differences is *false*?

    A. Within the same "race" there is an enormous amount of cultural variability.
    B. Members of any racial category are equally capable of learning any culture.
    C. Racial differences between human groups are a major cause of cultural differences between those same groups.
    D. Physical/"racial" differences between human groups are largely irrelevant in explaining the cultural differences between those groups.

27. The idea that groups of people differ in how they think, feel and act because they differ in their innate biological make up is called:

    A. cultural universals
    B. biological determinism
    C. evolutionary theory
    D. cultural integration

28. Anthropologists explain the differences between the Kikuyu culture and the Chinese culture by researching their:

    A. genetic differences
    B. racial differences
    C. biological differences
    D. cultural differences

29. Elements that exist in all human societies are known as:

    A. biological realities
    B. social enculturations
    C. cultural universals
    D. integrated cultures

30. Incest taboos are an example of:

    A. biological determinism
    B. cultural universals
    C. world view
    D. instinct

True / False Questions

1. Culture is the genetically transmitted knowledge that is shared by a group of people.

2. According to the anthropological definition, some of the world's peoples have "more culture" or have "better culture" than other peoples.

3. The main difference between apes and humans is brain size and intelligence.

4. The idea that humans evolved from an ape-like creature is purely theoretical, and has very little evidence to support it.

5. In the 1960s Jane Goodall observed chimpanzees using modified sticks as tools.

6. Scientists consider humans to be the most evolved species.

7. Cultural integration means the various parts of culture are mutually interdependent.

8. Modern cultural anthropologists think that the society in which we are enculturated more or less completely determines how we act.

9. When Semai children misbehave they are severely punished.

10. Culture is learned, not inborn.

11. Shaking hands when introduced to someone is an example of a norm.

12. Values are a people's beliefs about the way of life that is desirable for themselves and their society.

13. Symbols share the same meanings in almost every culture.

14. The Hanunoo in the Philippines identify only about 400 kinds of plants.

15. Some peoples in Micronesia point with their noses.

16. Most cultures share the same world view.

17. Norms and values provide clear guidelines for behavior.

18. According to biological determinism, cultural differences have a biological basis.

19. Human cultures are so diverse and variable that there are no such things as features found in all cultures.

20. Incest taboos are an example of cultural universals.

Multiple Choice Answers

1.	E	(p. 20)	16.	D	(p. 29-30)
2.	A	(p. 21)	17.	B	(p. 30)
3.	C	(p. 21)	18.	D	(p. 31)
4.	D	(p. 23)	19.	B	(p. 31)
5.	C	(p. 23)	20.	A	(p. 31)
6.	B	(p. 23)	21.	B	(p. 32)
7.	B	(p. 24)	22.	C	(p. 32)
8.	C	(p. 25)	23.	C	(p. 33)
9.	D	(p. 25)	24.	D	(p. 33-34)
10.	A	(p. 25-26)	25.	D	(p. 35)
11.	B	(p. 27)	26.	D	(p. 36)
12.	C	(p. 27)	27.	B	(p. 36)
13.	B	(p. 28)	28.	D	(p. 37)
14.	C	(p. 29)	29.	C	(p. 37)
15.	C	(p. 29)	30.	B	(p. 38)

True / False Answers

1.	F	(p. 20)	11.	T	(p. 29)
2.	F	(p. 20)	12.	T	(p. 29)
3.	F	(p. 21)	13.	F	(p. 30)
4.	F	(p. 21)	14.	F	(p. 31)
5.	T	(p. 22)	15.	T	(p. 30-31)
6.	F	(p. 23)	16.	F	(p. 32)
7.	T	(p. 25)	17.	F	(p. 35)
8.	F	(p. 26)	18.	T	(p. 36)
9.	F	(p. 27)	19.	F	(p. 37)
10.	T	(p. 27)	20.	T	(p. 38)

Chapter 3

CULTURE AND LANGUAGE

Multiple Choice Questions

1. *Homo sapiens* are the only animal capable of speech because

   A. no one has trained chimpanzees to speak
   B. other animals don't have any language capability
   C. only humans have a vocal tract that is biologically evolved for speech
   D. other animals don't need language as much as humans do.

2. Language is critical for humans because it

   A. shaped our biological evolution
   B. makes it possible for people to communicate and think about abstract concepts
   C. makes social learning by which children acquire culture possible
   D. all of the above

3. Which of the following is <u>not</u> a key property of language?

   A. proper grammar
   B. arbitrariness
   C. discrete and combinable units
   D. displacement

4. The ability to create totally novel sentences is called:

   A. arbitrariness
   B. productivity
   C. grammar
   D. discrete and combinable elements

5. Which of the following are the properties of language:

   A. multimedia potential, discreteness, arbitrariness, productivity, displacement
   B. multimedia potential, grammar, arbitrariness, productivity, displacement
   C. multimedia potential, discreteness, phonology, productivity
   D. discreteness, arbitrariness, productivity, displacement

6. The sounds and words in a language and the rules that govern how words are combined are called:

   A. phonetics
   B. arbitrariness
   C. grammar
   D. syntax

7. The variations in the grammar of a single language are called

   A. lexicons
   B. dialects
   C. phonemes
   D. morphemes

8. The smallest unit of sound recognized as distinctive from other sounds are called

   A. phonemes
   B. morphemes
   C. nasalizations
   D. bound morphemes

9. The difference between /p/ in mop and /b/ in boy is:

   A. whether our vocal cords vibrate or not
   B. one is voiced and the other isn't
   C. one is aspirated and the other isn't
   D. all of the above

10. Which of the following is known as a tone language

    A. Thai
    B. Burmese
    C. Vietnamese
    D. all of the above

11. Any sequence of phonemes that carries meaning is known as a

    A. lexicon
    B. tone
    C. morpheme
    D. a phoneme string

12. The study of the sounds and sound patterns of languages is called

    A. morphology
    B. grammar
    C. phonology
    D. ethnolinguistics

13. *Walk* is an example of a
    A. phoneme
    B. tone language
    C. free morpheme
    D. bound morpheme

14. How many morphemes are found in the word "unhealthful?"

   A. one
   B. two
   C. three
   D. four

15. Prefixes and suffixes like *bi-, dis-, -ing,* and *–s* are examples of

   A. phonemes
   B. tone languages
   C. free morphemes
   D. bound morphemes

16. Proxemics is the study of

   A. bodily motion in communication
   B. miscommunication
   C. the use of space in communication
   D. all of the above

17. The following is an example of nonverbal communication

   A. distance between two people
   B. smile
   C. wink
   D. all of the above

18. In the United States, personal distance is commonly

   A. Up to about 8 inches
   B. Just under a foot
   C. More than 2 feet to 4 feet
   D. Over four feet

19. The categorization and classification of livestock by American farmers is:

   A. organized in much the same way as elements of language
   B. an example of universal grammar
   C. biologically inaccurate
   D. not based on the age and sex of the animal

20. When speakers of a language need/want to communicate detailed information about things, qualities, people, and other entities of a common "type" or "category," the _____ of that category will develop a complex hierarchical structure.

   A. semantic domain
   B. phonemes
   C. world view
   D. sociolinguistics

21. A set of words such as, chair, table, sofa that belongs to an inclusive class (furniture) is a concept called:

A. semantic domain
B. free morphemes
C. Whorf-Sapir
D. honorifics

22. Which component of cultural knowledge is organized into patterns, much like the sound systems of language?

A. vocalizations
B. cognitive anthropology
C. classifications of reality
D. world views

23. The idea that language influences the perceptions and thought patterns of those who speak it and conditions their world view is knows as the

A. World View hypothesis
B. Classification of reality
C. Whorf-Sapir hypothesis
D. Concept of semantic dominance

24. The way the Hopi language affects how Hopi conceive of time and space is often cited as an example of

A. sociolinguistics
B. the Whorf-Sapir hypothesis
C. respect language
D. classification of reality

25. Social context and the use of speech is studied by the field of

A. ethnoscience
B. semantics
C. phonology
D. sociolinguistics

26. Which of the following are examples of topics studied by sociolinguists?

A. name taboos
B. how a person's gender affects his or her speech style
C. respect language
D. honorifics
E. all of the above

27. A recent estimate of how many languages have disappeared since the 15th century is:

   A. between 500 and 2,000
   B. between 2000 and 4,000
   C. between 4,000 and 9,000
   D. over 9,000

28. Which of the following languages has the most speakers
   A. English
   B. Mandarin
   C. Russian
   D. Welsh

29. The following is an example of a language taboo

   A. choosing a speech style according to the context
   B. using different pronouns when addressing a superior
   C. never uttering the name of deceased relatives in the presence of their kinfolk
   D. all of the above

30. Speech is affected by
   A. social context
   B. personal goals and how we present ourselves
   C. norms
   D. all of the above

True / False

1. Language has helped to shape our biological evolution.

2. The ability to recombine sounds into different sequences is known as productivity.

3. A speaker's ability to create completely novel sentences is known as arbitrariness.

4. According to most linguists, there's no such thing as "bad grammar."

5. Grammatical knowledge is unconscious and intuitive.

6. SAE or Standard American English is culturally accepted as most correct.

7. Anthropologists consider the southern dialect inferior.

8. The study of the sound system of language is called phonology.

9. Sounds made when the vocal cords vibrate are called voiced.

10. Some speakers cannot hear the difference between sounds such as /f/ and /v/.

11. In tone languages, the pitch of the voice makes a difference in the meaning of a word.

12. The total of all words in a language is called its morphology.

13. In the study of grammar, phonology refers to meaningful sound sequences and the rules by which they are formed.

14. Although all languages have words for concrete objects and events, languages differ markedly in their ability to express abstract concepts like *beauty* and *evil*.

15. When children say "goed", "runned" and "bringed", they are learning bad grammar.

16. Nonverbal communication includes how we touch others and how close we are to others when standing, sitting or walking.

17. The major interest of anthropological linguists is how the culture of a people is related to the language they speak.

18. Various peoples culturally classify their relatives or kin into *different* named categories that represent various "kinds of relatives."

19. Linguists recognize that some languages are more complex than others, in the sense that some are better able to communicate about subjects of concern to the speakers.

20. The semantic domain of "fish" is unlikely to be as elaborate among peoples who live in the desert as among coastal peoples.

21. The Whorf-Sapir hypothesis is widely accepted by most scholars today.

22. Sociolinguists study the history of languages.

23. In Polynesia there are distinct "levels" of speech, plain, more elegant and most elegant.

24. The 260 Native America languages spoken in Canada and the United States are very likely to be extinct within a few decades.

25. More people now speak English as their second language than as their first language.

Multiple Choice Answers

1.	C	(p. 42)	16.	C	(p. 51)
2.	D	(p. 42)	17.	D	(p. 51)
3.	A	(p. 43-44)	18.	C	(p. 52)
4.	B	(p. 44)	19.	A	(p. 52-53)
5.	A	(p. 43-44)	20.	A	(p. 53)
6.	C	(p. 44)	21.	A	(p. 53)
7.	B	(p. 45)	22.	C	(p. 53)
8.	A	(p. 46)	23.	C	(p. 55)
9.	D	(p. 46)	24.	B	(p. 55)
10.	D	(p. 48)	25.	D	(p. 57)
11.	C	(p. 49)	26.	E	(p. 57)
12.	C	(p. 46)	27.	C	(p. 58)
13.	C	(p. 49)	28.	B	(p. 59)
14.	C	(p. 49)	29.	C	(p. 60)
15.	D	(p. 49)	30.	D	(p. 61)

True / False Answers

1.	T	(p. 42)	14.	F	(p. 49)
2.	F	(p. 43)	15.	F	(p. 51)
3.	F	(p. 44)	16.	T	(p. 51)
4.	T	(p. 44)	17.	T	(p. 52)
5.	T	(p. 44)	18.	T	(p. 53)
6.	T	(p. 45)	19.	F	(p. 53)
7.	F	(p. 45)	20.	T	(p. 54)
8.	T	(p. 46)	21.	F	(p. 56)
9.	T	(p. 46)	22.	F	(p. 57)
10.	T	(p. 47)	23.	F	(p. 58)
11.	T	(p. 47)	24.	T	(p. 58)
12.	F	(p. 48)	25.	T	(p. 59)
13.	F	(p. 48)			

Chapter 4

ENCULTURATION AND THE LIFE CYCLE

Multiple choice

1. Which of the following are enculturation practices

    A. how children are nursed, held and weaned
    B. how parents interact with children
    C. behaviors that are punished and rewarded
    D. all of the above

2. Ju/'hoansi mothers consider it normal to

    A. threaten their children with kachinas or masked dancers
    B. breastfeed their children for about four years
    C. reward their children with toys and candy
    D. withhold affection from their children

3. The Aka are:

    A. pastoralists
    B. polygynous
    C. pygmies
    D. patrilocal

4. Which phrase best describes child care practices among the Aka of west Africa?

    A. stern fathers
    B. physical punishment
    C. multiple caretakers
    D. distant mothers

5. If an Aka parent strikes an infant

    A. the other parent has a reason to ask for a divorce
    B. they are practicing an ancient ritual
    C. they are scaring away evil spirits
    D. they are sent away until their children are grown

6. Which of the following is true about Aka fathers

    A. they rarely interact with their children
    B. they are not responsible for caring for infants
    C. they have the highest degree of father participation and involvement in infant care of any known human group
    D. none of the above

7. Which decentralized tribal people are patrilineal, polygynous, and patrilocal?

   A. Gusii of Kenya
   B. Apache of the American southwest
   C. Osages of Oklahoma
   D. Aka of west Africa

8. Gusii mothers often leave their infants with:

   A. their older siblings
   B. their fathers
   C. their grandparents
   D. other mothers

9. Polygyny is the practice of

   A. allowing women to have several husbands
   B. allowing men to have several wives
   C. passing the father's surname to the children
   D. living with the paternal family

10. Which statement does **not** distinguish child-rearing practices between the Aka and Gusii?

    A. Gusii mothers are more "bossy" towards their children than Aka mothers.
    B. Gusii mothers seem relatively emotionally distant from their older children.
    C. Gusii parents love their children less than Aka parents.
    D. Many Gusii fathers have several wives and spend a lot of time looking after their lands, livestock, and other resources, so are less involved with direct child care.

11. The comparison between Aka and Gusii shows that which of the following factors affect child-rearing practices?

    A. which sex owns or controls resources
    B. the relative important of warfare and organizing communities for offense and defense
    C. whether men are allowed to have more than one wife
    D. all of the above affect child-rearing practices

12. Which of the following is considered a rite of passage:

    A. wedding
    B. birthday
    C. graduation
    D. all of the above

13. Children are considered human among the Cheyenne when:

    A. in the womb
    B. after the mother felt the fetus kick
    C. when they are named
    D. when they have developed their first tooth

14. In her classic study, Coming of Age in Samoa, Margaret Mead found the following to be true:

    A. adolescence is a traumatic time in the life of Samoan girls
    B. adolescence is not a particularly traumatic time in the life of Samoan girls
    C. Samoan teens have as much trouble as American teens
    D. girls were helped through adolescence with elaborate initiation rites

15. Turner noted three phases of initiation rites:

    A. separation, liminality, incorporation
    B. separation, sacrifice, testing
    15. separation, scarification, socialization
    16. separation, initiation, marriage

16. Many New Guinea peoples believe

    A. females can pollute males
    B. males can pollute females
    C. adolescent girls should be separated from the group
    D. all of the above

17. Which of the following among the Awa boys of New Guinea is not a part of their puberty rites?

    A. they are beaten with stinging nettles
    B. their noses and penises are cut and pierced with sword grass and arrows
    C. they sweat for a week and then have their noses pierced with boar's tusks
    D. their hands are stung by scorpions to induce vomiting

18. Which people have painful and traumatic male initiation rituals?

    A. Aka of Africa
    B. Apache of North America
    C. Awa of Papua New Guinea
    D. Inuits of Canada

19. Which of the following societies is matrilineal?

    A. Gusii
    B. Aka
    C. Apache
    D. Inuit

20. Which people have female initiation rituals?

    A. Aka of Africa
    B. Mescalero Apache of North America
    C. Samoans of Polynesia
    D. Osage of Oklahoma

21. In many preindustrial societies, which event in the life cycle is most closely associated with ascending to the status of "full adult"?

   A. adolescence
   B. property ownership
   C. puberty rite
   D. marriage

22. Which of the following is considered the central function of marriage in most societies

   A. romance
   B. division of labor
   C. bearing children
   D. all of the above

23. Ethnographic studies show that modern attitudes toward the elderly

   A. are less compassionate than in the past
   B. are much less respectful than in the past
   C. are more respectful than in the past
   D. are about the same as they were in the past

24. Elderly persons in social cultures were sometimes:

   A. abandoned
   B. killed by a close relative
   C. victims of pranks
   D. all of the above

25. The elderly receive the greatest respect in societies where
   A. the elderly control the resources
   B. the young are taught to respect their elders
   C. the elderly can be left alone and taken care of by the others
   D. the elderly need the most help

True-False

1. The mothers of some cultures coat their nipples with bitter substances to discourage nursing after a certain age.

2. Fathers are almost never involved in child care in human societies.

3. Hopi children are never threatened by kachinas to get them to behave.

4. Aka fathers are as involved and sometimes more involved in the care of infants as Aka mothers.

5. Aka men commonly flaunt their talents and brag about their accomplishments.

6.   Gusii fathers are barely involved in caring for their children.

7.   Only American parents understand the importance of "quality time" with their children.

8.   Every culture studied so far maintains that human life begins at birth.

9.   In some cultures such as Osage, infants are not recognized as "social persons" until they receive a name.

10.   In the 1920s, Margaret Mead claimed that adolescence was not particularly traumatic in Samoa.

11.   The key purpose of puberty rites is to mark a person's sexual maturation.

12.   Peoples everywhere ceremonially recognize the various stages in the lives of individuals by rites of passage. Surprisingly all cultures recognize the same stages.

13.   The Awa of New Guinea believe that women are pure and warn that men can pollute them.

14.   The male initiation rites of the Awa are typical of rites in other cultures.

15.   Male initiation rites around the world are commonly painful and traumatic.

16.   Female initiation rites are less common and most often emphasize their adult duties as wives and mothers.

17.   Puberty rites for Mescalero Apache girls last for 4 months.

18.   The Inuit would often have someone stay behind to take care of their elderly when they were unable to travel.

19.   In most societies, bearing and rearing children is one of the central functions of marriage.

20.   Unlike industrialized nations, practically all preindustrial peoples honor the elderly and give them positions of authority.

Multiple Choice Answers

1.	D	(p. 66)	14.	B	(p. 76)
2.	B	(p. 66)	15.	A	(p. 76)
3.	C	(p. 68)	16.	A	(p. 77)
4.	C	(p. 68)	17.	D	(p. 77)
5.	A	(p. 68)	18.	C	(p. 77)
6.	C	(p. 68)	19.	C	(p. 78)
7.	A	(p. 69)	20.	B	(p. 78)
8.	A	(p, 69)	21.	D	(p. 79)
9.	B	(p. 70)	22.	C	(p. 79)
10.	B	(p. 71)	23.	D	(p. 80)
11.	D	(p. 71-72)	24.	D	(p. 79)
12.	D	(p. 73)	25.	A	(p. 80)
13.	A	(p. 74)			

True / False Answers

1.	T	(p. 66)	11.	F	(p. 76)
2.	F	(p. 67)	12.	F	(p.73)
3.	F	(p. 67)	13.	F	(p. 78)
4.	T	(p. 68)	14.	F	(p.78)
5.	F	(p. 69)	15.	T	(p. 78)
6.	T	(p. 70)	16.	T	(p. 78)
7.	F	(p.72)	17.	F	(p. 78)
8.	F	(p. 74)	18.	F	(p.79)
9.	T	(p. 74)	19.	T	(p. 79)
10.	T	(p. 75)	20.	F	(p. 79)

Chapter 5

THE DEVELOPMENT OF ANTHROPOLOGICAL THOUGHT

Multiple Choice Questions

1. Some changes which led to the beginnings and growth of anthropology are:

    A. unilineal and multilineal evolutionism
    B. evidence that the earth was older than suggested by the scriptures and Darwinism
    C. historical particularism and functionalism
    D. Marxism and cultural materialism

2. Factors that led to greater acceptance of Darwin's theory of evolution include:

    A. scholars found that evolution explained so much
    B. discoveries in Africa in the 1920s confirmed Darwin's hypothesis
    C. it was possible to find evidence of evolutionary "stages" in the fossil record
    D. all of the above

3. Anthropology developed in the late 1800s as European scholars tried to understand peoples and cultures in the lands they colonized. Which nineteenth century approach used concepts such as "stages" and "progress" to understand cultural differences?

    A. unilineal evolutionism
    B. historical particularism
    C. interpretive anthropology
    D. postmodernism

4. The belief that nature is populated by supernatural beings such as ghosts, souls, demons, and nature spirits is called:

    A. superstition
    B. science
    C. animism
    D. evolution

5. E. B. Tylor argued in his book that religion passed through three stages:

    A. cults, Christianity, evolution
    B. animism, polytheism, monotheism
    C. animism, superstition, science
    D. unilineal evolution, historical particularism, materialism

6. The first anthropology department was founded at:

    A. Berkeley
    B. University of Rochester
    C. Harvard
    D. University of Pennsylvania

7. This approach emphasized that each culture is a unique product of its past, and so must be looked at in its own terms rather than seen as a representative of its "stage."

   A. historical particularism
   B. British functionalism
   C. modern materialism
   D. unilineal evolutionism

8. Which approach did the most to formulate and strengthen the perspective called cultural relativism?

   A. historical particularism
   B. unilineal evolutionism
   C. mid-century evolutionism
   D. British functionalism

9. A key contribution of historical particularism to modern anthropology was:

   A. insistence on fieldwork as primary means of acquiring reliable information
   B. idea that cultural relativism is essential in understanding another culture
   C. demonstration that cultural and biological differences have little to do with one another
   D. all of the above

10. The study of how cultural elements are transmitted from one people or region to another is called

    A. configurationalism
    B. diffusionism
    C. patterns of culture
    D. relativism

11. One contribution of Boas was:

    A. his emphasis on fieldwork
    B. his relativistic approach to other cultures
    C. his training of other well-known anthropologists
    D. all of the above

12. According to Benedict, the Zuni of the North American Southwest:

    A. control their emotions
    B. are social and cooperative
    C. do not boast
    D. all of the above

13. Which approach most emphasized the integration of cultural systems, and helped make cultural anthropology holistic?

A. unilineal evolutionism
B. historical particularism
C. British functionalism
D. modern materialism

14. Which approach assumed that the basic purpose of culture is to meet the needs of individuals and/or of society as a whole, since society is "like a living organism"?

A. historical particularism
B. British functionalism
C. mid-century evolutionism
D. materialism

15. A. R. Radcliffe-Brown was a:

A. functionalist
B. cultural materialist
C. unilineal evolutionist
D. an evolutionist

16. Malinowski was:

A. an important British functionalist
B. an important British materialist
C. wrote an ethnography of the Trobrianders, Argonauts of the Western Pacific
D. a geologist

17. The idea that the whole purpose of culture is to serve human biological and psychological needs was argued by:

A. Malinowski
B. Boas
C. Benedict
D. Radcliffe-Brown

18. One of Radcliffe-Brown's contributions to modern anthropology was his:

A. holistic perspective
B. emphasis on technological progress
C. emphasis on what goes on in human minds rather than on what goes into their stomachs
D. all of the above

19. Which two men led the mid-century revival of evolutionary approaches, by arguing that we can best explain cultures by "technological determinism" or "techno-environmental determinism"?

A. E.B. Tylor and Charles Darwin
B. Franz Boas and Ruth Benedict
C. Bronislaw Malinowski and A.R. Radcliffe-Brown
D. Leslie White and Julian Steward

20. Julian Steward was:

A. a technological determinist
B. an idealist
C. a techno-environmental determinist
D. an historical particularist

21. A major division in anthropology today is between:

A. creationists and evolutionists
B. generalists and particularists
C. unilineal evolutionists and British functionalists
D. science and humanism

22. Which statement does *not* characterize the modern humanistic approach?

A. Because humans are cultural beings, they differ in kind from other animals.
B. In studying others, we should interact and participate, not measure and quantify.
C. Every culture must be treated as unique, for comparisons are sure to distort and mislead.
D. Two well-trained, unbiased fieldworkers who study the same culture at the same time will agree on their findings. If not, one or both is "wrong."

23. The basic imperative of materialism is:

A. Like all animals, human groups must adapt to the conditions in their natural environments
B. Culture differences can not be explained by material needs and satisfaction
C. All knowledge is relative
D. Each human culture is unique

24. Which modern approach holds that factors like technology, natural environment, and resources can potentially explain cultural differences and similarities?

A. British functionalism
B. historical particularism
C. interpretive anthropology
D. materialism

25. Idealists:

   A. are idealistic in their approach to anthropology
   B. think the ideas and beliefs of a culture are fundamental in making it the way it is
   C. think cultures are simple and easily explained
   D. all of the above

26. Idealists claim materialist explanations fail because:

   A. resources are culturally defined, not inherent in nature
   B. people's perception of the world is not as important to their adaptation as the conditions of their environment
   C. material needs are more important to humans than social needs
   D. all of the above

27. Interpretive anthropologists:

   A. stress the scientific approach to the study of culture
   B. emphasize the uniqueness and individuality of each human culture
   C. recognize that different elements of a culture are strongly influenced by material conditions
   D. seek generalized explanations of human ways of life

28. The approach used by anthropologists who study mythology, art, oral traditions, or world view is probably:

   A. materialistic
   B. idealistic
   C. postmodernist
   D. systemic

29. Factors that affect how a community responds to a fieldworker include:

   A. the fieldworker's physical characteristics
   B. the experience the community had had with other fieldworkers
   C. the questions the fieldworker asks
   D. all of the above

30. Modern anthropologists cannot agree on even certain fundamental issues, such as whether their field is more like the "sciences" or the "humanities." What is the reason for this disagreement?

   A. despite their training, fieldworkers go into their research with biases, making objectivity difficult to achieve.
   B. we cannot set up controlled experiments while in the field.
   C. anthropology is so broad that it attracts a wide range of people who want to study a huge variety of subjects.
   D. all of the above are reasons why those anthropologists can't agree

True / False Questions

1. Until the mid-1800s the customs and beliefs of distant peoples were interpreted in terms of the biblical account of world creation and human history.

2. In his book, *On the Origin of Species*, Charles Darwin proposed that men evolved from monkeys.

3. Unilineal evolutionists thought that cultures could be ranked by their complexity.

4. According to E. B. Tylor, the two questions that puzzled the earliest cultures were 1) what is the difference between a live person and a dead person? and 2) what is the origin of my own fears?

5. Boas believed that fieldwork was useful, but not essential.

6. Historical particularists agreed with E.B. Tylor that human religion passed through three stages in its development: animism, polytheism, and monotheism.

7. The idea that each culture develops a distinctive set of feelings and motivations that orients the thoughts and behaviors of its members is called diffusionism.

8. Functionalism is the idea that the cultural features of a people can be explained by the functions they perform.

9. Radcliffe-Brown believed that the purpose of a culture was to serve human biological and psychological needs.

10. Because of the work of anthropologists like Boas and Malinowski, the fieldwork experience is an important part of the graduate training of almost all anthropologists.

11. According to Malinowski, the main objective of fieldwork is to see the culture as an insider to the culture sees it.

12. Technological determinists believe the technology available to a people has little impact on other aspects of their culture.

13. Julian Steward argued that technology and the environment play large roles in shaping a culture.

14. Modern cultural anthropologists think that culture is more like a "text" than a "thing."

15. Materialists think that a culture's ideas help make it the way it is more so than its environmental adaptation.

16. Most idealists are skeptical of scientific explanations of a culture.

17. Interpretive anthropologists see all social interaction as symbolic and meaningful.

18. Idealists claim that natural resources are culturally defined (culturally constructed), so they have very little importance in making cultures the way they are.

19. Scholars who specialize in human adaptation, economic systems, or long-term evolutionary changes in societies are likely to use a materialistic approach.

20. Although ethnologists in the past disagreed about whether cultures can be compared and eventually explained, this is not an important question in cultural anthropology today.

Multiple Choice Answers

1.	B	(p. 84)
2.	D	(p. 84)
3.	A	(p. 85)
4.	C	(p. 86)
5.	B	(p. 86)
6.	D	(p. 87)
7.	A	(p. 87)
8.	A	(p. 88)
9.	D	(p. 88)
10.	B	(p. 88)
11.	D	(p. 87-88)
12.	D	(p. 88-89)
13.	C	(p. 89-90)
14.	B	(p. 89)
15.	A	(p. 90)
16.	A	(p. 90)
17.	A	(p. 89)
18.	A	(p. 90-91)
19.	D	(p. 91)
20.	C	(p. 92)
21.	D	(p. 92-94)
22.	D	(p. 94)
23.	A	(p. 94)
24.	D	(p. 94)
25.	B	(p. 95)
26.	A	(p. 97)
27.	B	(p. 97)
28.	B	(p. 98)
29.	D	(p. 100)
30.	D	(p. 100)

True / False Answers

1.	T	(p. 84)
2.	F	(p. 84)
3.	T	(p. 85)
4.	F	(p. 86)
5.	F	(p. 87)
6.	F	(p. 87)
7.	F	(p. 88)
8.	T	(p. 89)
9.	F	(p. 89)
10.	T	p. 91)
11.	T	(p. 91)
12.	F	(p. 91)
13.	T	(p. 91-92)
14.	F	(p. 93)
15.	F	(p. 95)
16.	T	(p. 95)
17.	T	(p. 97)
18.	T	(p. 97)
19.	T	(p. 98)
20.	F	(p. 99)

Chapter 6

METHODS OF INVESTIGATION

Multiple Choice Questions

1. The two broad categories of anthropological methods are comparative and:

    A. participant observation
    B. interviewing
    C. consultants
    D. ethnographic

2. The study of the culture of a people by using written records, pictures, maps, and other records is called:

    A. ethnographic research
    B. ethnohistoric research
    C. record studies
    D. historical fieldwork

3. Ethnographic research that involves observing and interviewing the members of a culture to describe their contemporary way of life is called:

    A. cross-cultural comparisons
    B. fieldwork
    C. ethnohistoric research
    D. contemporary observations

4. Structured interviews:

    A. often include open-ended questions
    B. collect the most cultural data
    C. consist of a limited number of specific questions
    D. are better than participant observation

5. Ethnographic fieldwork consists of:

    A. interviewing
    B. observing
    C. participating in activities
    D. all of the above

6. The idea of participant observation as a field research technique was developed by:

    A. Bronislaw Malinowski
    B. Margaret Mead
    C. Edward Tylor
    D. John L. Lewis

7.   The ethics of fieldwork:

   A. state, in part, that anthropologists must take care not to harm the local people who provided information
   B. demand that anthropologists tell local people who is exploiting them
   C. require anthropologists to agree with all of the local people's morals
   D. are neither a concern to local people nor to the anthropologist

8.   Which of the following are difficulties in every field research situation:

   A. identifying and interviewing consultants
   B. defining the fieldworker's role in the community
   C. stereotyping
   D. all of the above

9.   Often, anthropologists develop a rapport with the members of the community being studied:

   A. quickly and without any problems
   B. and are soon totally accepted by the community
   C. against a background of suspicion and distrust
   D. only after taking part in initiation rites

10.   The member of a culture who gives information to a researcher is called a:

   A. informant
   B. friend
   C. tribal counsel
   D. ethnohistorian

11.   Fieldwork is important to cultural anthropologists because it is a major source of data on human cultures and:

   A. it is a key aspect of the anthropologist's education
   B. it is usually a fun, easy way to travel and see the world
   C. it is one of the more enjoyable aspects of the profession
   D. allows the anthropologist to truly become a part of another culture.

12.   The San peoples:

   A. are suing for royalties over a diet pill
   B. formed WIMSA to protect their intellectual property rights
   C. live in South Africa
   D. all of the above

13.   The Pueblos of the Rio Grande Valley of New Mexico are secretive of their:

   A. genealogies
   B. traditional beliefs and rituals
   C. cooking techniques
   D. myths and legends

14. Anthropologists face many problems in the course of field research. These problems may include:

    A. stereotyping
    B. developing a role and rapport
    C. identifying consultants
    D. culture shock
    E. all of the above

15. Which are the symptoms of culture shock?

    A. Paranoia
    B. Anxiety
    C. Homesickness
    D. Nausea
    E. All of the above

16. An ethnohistorian is primarily interested in:

    A. reconstructing actual historical events
    B. studying the written records of literate peoples
    C. the ethnocentrism of the records
    D. reconstructing the cultural system of the people

17. A difficult with ethnohistory is:

    A. ethnocentrism
    B. there are no clear rules for evaluating the data
    C. there is no simple way to evaluate a document or account.
    D. all of the above

18. The basic aims of ethnographic methods are:

    A. descriptive
    B. relative
    C. comparative
    D. theoretical

19. Comparative methods of anthropology are used to:

    A. describe particular cultural systems
    B. collect cultural data on peoples
    C. explain why differences exist between cultures
    D. focus on the cultural traits of a single society

20. The main purpose of cross-cultural comparative studies is:

    A. to describe the culture of a particular people in detail
    B. to test hypothesis
    C. to generate new ideas for field researchers to study
    D. all of the above

21. The comparative study that investigated the relationship between sorcery and legal systems found that:

    A. where sorcery was unimportant, a specialized legal apparatus was usually present
    B. where sorcery was unimportant, a specialized legal apparatus was usually absent
    C. where sorcery was important, a specialized legal apparatus was usually present
    D. there was no correlation between the importance of sorcery and the presence of a specialized legal apparatus

22. When an anthropologist says that one sociocultural element, "A," is correlated with another element, "B," that researcher means:

    A. A caused B to come into existence
    B. B caused A to come into existence
    C. whenever A is present, B is usually present
    D. both A and B were brought into existence by a third unknown factor

23. Which of the following is a problem with cross-cultural studies:

    A. the *Ethnographic Atlas* only lists one cultural system for each culture
    B. grouping variables such as cultures that are monotheistic
    C. testing hypotheses
    D. both a and b above

24. The finding that matrilineal societies are more successful than patrilineal societies among the Native American cultures of the eastern U.S. means:

    A. the matrilineal societies maintained a higher percentage of their population than the patrilineal societies
    B. the matrilineal societies tried to destroy the patrilineal societies
    C. the patrilineal societies never had a larger population than the matrilineal societies
    D. the matrilineal societies were less successful than the patrilineal societies in adapting to European contact

25. The primary purpose of controlled historical comparisons is:

    A. collect descriptive data
    B. collect data from living individuals
    C. document changes in particular groupings of societies over time
    D. focus on many cultures and their differences

True-False Questions

1. Fieldwork has always been the primary method used by anthropologists to collect cultural information.

2. Unstructured interviews are best suited for collecting quantitative data about a group.

3. A structured interview may be a questionnaire.

4. The technique of participant observation was introduced as a new data-collection technique for anthropologists by Bronislaw Malinowski.

5. While anthropologists have moral obligations to their profession, their first obligation is to get the information they need to complete their study.

6. Since ethnographers can learn much about people simply by living among them and participating in their activities, interviewing consultants is not usually necessary.

7. Sometimes informants may deliberately try to deceive the researcher.

8. Most communities in the world recognize the importance of anthropological research, and thus openly welcome the researcher.

9. One of the major problems faced by ethnohistorians, is that the records on which they have to depend for gaining an understanding of a people, were written by individuals who had at best, an imperfect understanding of their culture, and in many cases were openly hostile to their believes and cultural behavior.

10. Captain Cook was killed by Hawaiians because he was caught looting sacred relics.

11. Anthropologists use comparative methods to study the cultural variables in a single society.

12. Whiting found support for her hypothesis that sorcery is important in societies that lack police and a court system.

13. Controlled historical comparisons use changes in particular groupings of societies over time to define general cultural patterning and test hypotheses.

14. Ethnohistorians have found that some non-Western societies have changed far more dramatically over the past centuries than had previously been thought.

15. Cross-cultural comparisons and controlled historical comparisons provide very similar measures of cultural phenomena.

Multiple Choice Answers

1.	D	(p. 103)
2.	B	(p. 104)
3.	B	(p. 104)
4.	C	(p. 104-105)
5.	D	(p. 104-105)
6.	A	(p. 105)
7.	A	(p. 106)
8.	D	(p. 106-107)
9.	C	(p. 106-107)
10.	A	(p. 107)
11.	A	(p. 110)
12.	D	(p. 109)
13.	B	(p. 110)
14.	E	(p. 110)
15.	E	(p. 111)
16.	D	(p. 111)
17.	D	(p. 111-112)
18.	A	(p. 104)
19.	C	(p. 113)
20.	B	(p. 113)
21.	A	(p. 113-115)
22.	C	(p. 114)
23.	D	(p. 113-115)
24.	A	(p. 116-117)
25.	C	(p. 116)

True / False Answers

1.	T	(p. 104)
2.	F	(p. 104)
3.	T	(p. 104)
4.	T	(p. 105)
5.	F	(p. 106)
6.	F	(p. 107)
7.	T	(p. 108)
8.	F	(p. 111)
9.	T	(p. 111)
10.	F	(p. 112-113)
11.	F	(p. 113)
12.	T	(p. 114)
13.	T	(p. 115)
14.	T	(p. 115)
15.	F	(p. 117)

Chapter 7

ADAPTATION: ENVIRONMENT AND CULTURES

Multiple Choice Questions

1. Human populations adapt to their environments:

    A. physiologically
    B. genetically
    C. culturally
    D. all of the above

2. The three components of production are labor, resources and:

    A. time
    B. climate
    C. technology
    D. land

3. The three factors of the organization of production are division of labor, patterns of cooperation and:

    A. food taboos
    B. technology
    C. marriage rules
    D. rights of access

4. In preindustrial societies, property is frequently:

    A. non-existent
    B. owned by individuals
    C. owned by a group
    D. fought over

5. Anthropologists divide preindustrial adaptations based on how people:

    A. live in groups
    B. structure their families
    C. produce their food supply
    D. all of the above

6. Foragers get their food from:

    A. gathering
    B. hunting
    C. fishing
    D. all of the above

7. Homo sapiens:

    A. started farming one million years ago
    B. only existed as a species 10,000 years ago
    C. survived by foraging for the first 90 to 95% of our existence as a species
    D. as a genus was not around until 6,000 years ago

8. Among most foragers, the division of labor (who does what kinds of tasks) is based on all the following except:

    A. social rank or class
    B. gender
    C. skill and knowledge
    D. sex

9. Which of these characterizes the cultures of most hunter-gatherers?

    A. small, mobile ("nomadic") living groups
    B. land (that is, hunting and gathering territory) is owned by individual families
    C. meat is rarely shared between families because of the shortage of protein
    D. the division of labor is determined by social rank and status differences between families

10. A band:

    A. is constant in size numbering about 500 individuals
    B. is usually strongly territorial over its environmental resources
    C. typically shares food and other possessions among its members
    D. is a mobile group of about 50 people

11. Which behavior is likely to be positively valued (and rewarded) among foragers?

    A. competing
    B. boasting
    C. sharing
    D. accumulating

12. The main way the Inuit ("Eskimo") differ from most other foragers is:

    A. their seasonal mobility
    B. sharing of meat within the camp
    C. high dependence on animal flesh (meat) for food
    D. lack of domesticated animals

13. The cultures of the Northwest Coast Indians differed from those of most other foragers in that:

   A. their dwellings were more finely built and permanent
   B. they were more sedentary
   C. they had social ranks
   D. Northwest Coast peoples differed in all the ways listed above, because of their unusually productive environment

14. Domestication refers to:

   A. intentional planting of plants for food
   B. intentional planting of plants for drugs
   C. the breeding of animals for food
   D. all of the above

15. Domestication first arose in the New World how many years ago?

   A. 2,000 years ago
   B. 5,000 years ago
   C. 10,000 years ago
   D. 15,000 years ago

16. One advantage of agriculture over hunting and gathering is that it:

   A. can support a higher population density than foraging
   B. takes much less time and energy than foraging
   C. follows the "10 percent rule" whereas pastoralism does not
   D. all of the above

17. Horticulture is a type of farming that uses:

   A. plows pulled by draft animals
   B. mechanical irrigation equipment
   C. hand tools and human power
   D. none of the above

18. Slash and burn and dry land gardening are examples of:

   A. hunting and gathering (foraging)
   B. horticulture
   C. intensive agriculture
   D. pastoralism

19. Horticulturalists differ from hunters and gatherers in that:

   A. horticulturalists usually live in villages, often with hundreds of members
   B. horticulturalists are usually much more sedentary
   C. families in horticultural societies have better-defined rights to specific lands ("fields")
   D. all of the above are differences between horticulturalists and foragers

20. The Pueblo peoples of the Southwest reduced the risk of cultivation by:

A. planting corn in areas most likely to flood
B. planting crops in areas least likely to wash away during severe flooding
C. planting crops weeks apart to avoid untimely frost
D. all of the above

21. The first plant domestication occurred in Southwest Asia in an area often called the:

A. Fertile Crescent
B. Mediterranean
C. Ethiopian highlands
D. coastal lowlands

22. One way the cultures of horticulturists differ from foragers:

A. living groups are larger
B. living groups are more permanently settled
C. families have more definite rights of ownership
D. all of the above

23. Highly complex societies, including states and civilizations, require that peasant farmers produce a large surplus. Therefore, complex societies only develop with which adaptation?

A. hunting and gathering
B. horticulture
C. intensive agriculture
D. fishing

24. One of the characteristics of pastoralism is:

A. nomadism
B. the payment of tribute to the state
C. that pastoralists take land away from cultivators
D. their frequent barbecues

25. Which of the following people adapt to their environment mainly by pastoralism?

A. the Pueblo Indians of the American southwest
B. peasants of the ancient world
C. the Western Shoshone of the United States
D. the Karimojong of East Africa

26. Pastoralists (livestock herders) are located primarily in which kinds of environments?

A. tropical forests, where there are many leaves for the animals to eat
B. temperate regions, where there is a lot of rainfall
C. arid or cold regions, where cultivation is impossible or difficult
D. arctic regions, where no other way of life is possible

27. The 10% rule states that:

    A. only about 10% of the energy locked up in living matter at one level is available to the next level.
    B. only about 10% of any given herd of herbivores will survive for 10 years.
    C. people need to gather 10% of their food in order to keep their environment healthy.
    D. all of the above

28. The foraging adaptation is most efficient when:

    A. people live in small mobile groups
    B. people own land and protect it from others
    C. a people is settled in one area
    D. none of the above

29. Towns and cities resulted from:

    A. pastoral peoples that decided to create work groups
    B. foragers who always had more than they could eat
    C. surplus caused by intensive agriculture
    D. herders who wanted to protect their land

30. Horticulturalists lived in:

    A small bands of between 10 and 50 people
    B Cities and town surrounded by "peasant" communities
    C Scattered hamlets or villages of 100 or more
    D seasonally nomadic living units of varying size

True / False Questions

1. Like other animals, biological/genetic changes are the main way in which people adapt to new environments or to environmental changes.

2. The three components of production are labor, technology and resources.

3. Anthropologists divide preindustrial adaptations into three categories based largely on how people live in social groups.

4. Foraging (or hunting and gathering) nourished humanity for most of our existence.

5. Compared to people who live by other adaptations, hunters and gatherers have the most control over their natural environments.

6. Evidence about the hunting and gathering way of life generally shows that they had to work very hard and long to acquire their food and were usually malnourished and unhealthy.

7. The division of labor by foragers is organized largely along the lines of age and sex.

8. Traditional Shoshone gathered in bands during the winter to eat pine nuts.

9.   In a foraging band, people who regularly fail to share are subject to ridicule and other social pressures.

10.   Many cultural features of the Plains Indians did not exist until after the introduction of the buffalo into North America.

11.   The nineteenth century culture of the Plains Indians, featuring tipis and bison hunting from horseback, was the way the people had lived for thousands of years.

12.   Dr. Lee found that the average !Kung works longer hours than the average American,

13.   Among the !Kung of southern Africa, band size remained pretty constant throughout the year, despite changes in the seasons and rainfall.

14.   The characteristic technology of horticulture is using only human power and hand tools.

15.   Shifting cultivation is a form of horticulture where a plot is cultivated for only 2 to 3 years before it is abandoned.

16.   Two foods that commonly appear on American dinner plates – cattle flesh (beef) and wheat (made into bread) -- were first domesticated in the Fertile Crescent of modern Iraq, Jordan, and Syria.

17.   Horticulture differs from foraging in that families have more rights of ownership over land and living groups are larger and more permanently settled.

18.   Horticulture is more likely to produce a food surplus than intensive agriculture.

19.   The "10 percent rule" says that only about 10% of the energy locked up in living matter at one level is available to the next level.

20.   One of the reasons the Maasai continue their cattle herding rather than cultivate crops is their cultural heritage.

Multiple Choice Answers

1.	D	(p. 122)		16.	A	(p. 130)
2.	C	(p. 122)		17.	C	(p. 131)
3.	D	(p. 122-123		18.	B	(p. 131)
4.	C	(p. 123)		19.	D	(p. 131-133
5.	C	(p. 123)		20.	D	(p. 132-133)
6.	D	(p. 123		21.	A	(p. 133)
7.	C	(p. 123)		22.	D	(p. 134)
8.	A	(p. 124)		23.	C	(p. 135)
9.	A	(p. 124)		24.	A	(p. 139
10.	D	(p. 126)		25.	D	(p. 142)
11.	C	(p. 127)		26.	C	(p. 139)
12.	C	(p. 128)		27.	A	(p. 141)
13.	D	(p. 128)		28.	A	(p. 143)
14.	D	(p. 128-129)		29.	C	(p. 143)
15.	C	(p. 144)		30.	C	(p. 143)

True / False Answers

1.	F	(p. 122)		11.	F	(p.128)
2.	T	(p. 122)		12.	F	(p. 131)
3.	F	(p. 123)		13.	F	(p. 131)
4.	T	(p. 124)		14.	T	(p. 131)
5.	F	(p. 124)		15.	T	(p. 131)
6.	F	(p. 124-125)		16.	T	(p. 132-133)
7.	T	(p. 124)		17.	T	(p. 135)
8.	F	(p. 125)		18.	F	(p. 136)
9.	T	(p. 127)		19.	T	(p. 142)
10.	F	(p. 128)		20.	T	(p. 141

Chapter 8

EXCHANGE IN ECONOMIC SYSTEMS

Multiple Choice Questions

1. How people allocate their labor, technology and resources is part of their:

    A. reciprocity
    B. economic system
    C. marketplace
    D. market economy

2. Which form of exchange is organized by a central authority such as a leader or government?

    A. negative reciprocity
    B. redistribution
    C. balanced reciprocity
    D. market

3. The form of exchange that occurs in some form in all human populations is:

    A. reciprocity
    B. redistribution
    C. market
    D. all of the above

4. The type of economic system that requires money and private property is:

    A. redistribution
    B. reciprocity
    C. market
    D. all of the above

5. Which of the following is a form of reciprocity:

    A. giving a gift
    B. bartering
    C. sharing with those in need
    D. all of the above

6. Providing children with food and shelter is an example of:

    A. redistribution
    B. pork barrel
    C. exchange spheres as among the Tiv
    D. generalized reciprocity

7. Which form of exchange is dominant in small bands in which all or most members are relatives?

A. generalized reciprocity
B. balanced reciprocity
C. negative reciprocity
D. redistribution

8. Which form of exchange is most commonly used to create or sustain political and/or military alliances?

A. generalized reciprocity
B. balanced reciprocity
C. negative reciprocity
D. redistribution

9. Trade partnerships like *wasi* in the Trobriands are examples of :

A. generalized reciprocity
B. balanced reciprocity
C. peasant marketplaces
D. money exchanged for products and services

10. Which of the following statements about the characteristics of balanced reciprocity is true?

A. persons involved in the exchange bargain to get the best deal
B. the relationship between the parties involved may be jeopardized if items or favors are not reciprocated
C. the most common reason for this exchange is to help a person out
D. this form of exchange is not found in all societies because authority does not exist in all societies

11. Which people have the custom they call "insulting the meat"?

A. the !Kung
B. the Tiv
C. the Maring
D. the Micronesians

12. In which type of exchange do both parties attempt to gain all they can from the exchange while giving up as little as possible?

A. generalized reciprocity
B. balanced reciprocity
C. redistribution
D. negative reciprocity

13. The type of reciprocity that occurs between individuals or groups depends on:

   A. social distance between them
   B. type of control exerted by the chief
   C. amount of taxes or tribute collected
   D. supply and demand

14. A tribute is a common form of:

   A. exchange
   B. balanced reciprocity
   C. redistribution
   D. generalized reciprocity

15. Redistribution differs from reciprocity in that:

   A. reciprocity is only found in egalitarian societies
   B. redistribution usually involves transactions in cash
   C. redistribution is characteristic of societies that produce very little surplus
   D. redistribution is a form of exchange that requires a third party as an intermediary between giver and receiver

16. The following is an example of redistribution:

   A. taxes
   B. wedding gifts
   C. bartering
   D. shared feasting

17. Which of the following statements about redistribution is true?

   A. in modern nations, unlike some preindustrial societies, tax revenues are used entirely for the public good
   B. in some preindustrial societies, unlike modern societies, taxes are used entirely for the public good
   C. tax revenues in both preindustrial societies and modern nations are sometimes used for the public good rather than for selfish purposes
   D. none of the above statements is true

18. Which exchange form requires money and prices?

   A. negative reciprocity
   B. market
   C. redistribution
   D. generalized reciprocity

19. Money and prices determined by supply and demand must be present before _____ can exist.

   A. reciprocity
   B. redistribution
   C. market
   D. all of the above

20. The role of government in a market is to:

   A. print money and control the money supply
   B. protect private property
   C. pay for public goods and infrastucture
   D. all of the above

21. Which of the following is true about the idea of money:

   A. money serves as a media of exchange
   B. money serves as a standard of value
   C. money is a store of value
   D. money has symbolic significance
   E. all of the above

22. Which of the following is <u>not</u> an example of money?

   A. red bird feathers
   B. metal rods
   C. shells
   D. none of the above

23. Limited-purpose money is illustrated by:

   A. barter in the Trobriand islands
   B. pig feasts among the Maring of Papua New Guinea
   C. tribute in Micronesia and Polynesia
   D. metal rods among the Tiv of Nigeria

24. In a market economy:

   A. only the most prized good and services have a monetary price
   B. most people make their living off the land
   C. the economy is regulated by a governing board
   D. none of the above

25. Which of the following is an example of a way that living in a market economy affects people and society:

   A. You never need to work and you have access to a territory that supplies everything you need.
   B. No one you know has very many material possessions, everyone has about the same things and there is no media telling you that you need more.
   C. Advertising constantly reminds you that you want things you never knew existed.
   D. You have no concept of wage or job security.

26. One characteristic of a peasant marketplace is:

   A. peasant families rely on the marketplace for most of their needs
   B. vendors in the marketplace often develop personal relationships with their customers
   C. marketplaces are open every day and have a wide variety of products
   D. most people make their living by selling their items in the marketplace

27. The internationalization of capital and labor aspect of market globalization refers to:

   A. ending tariffs and quotas on consumer goods
   B. the hope that all countries will use the Eurodollar
   C. moving factories to regions where the labor is cheap
   D. government monopolies

28. In the 1960's, an agreement between the U.S. and Mexico:

   A. Allowed U.S. corporations to set up factories in Mexico along the border region with Texas.
   B. Allowed components to be made in the United States, exported back to Mexico for assembly, then finished and sold in the U.S.
   C. Removed any tariffs on the finished products.
   D. All of the above.

29. The real winner from globalization is/are:

   A. factory workers
   B. cultural diversity
   C. corporations
   D. the environment

30. *Suki* in the Philippines helps to:

   A. increase the long-term economic security of peasant vendors (sellers)
   B. increase the prices of goods to consumers in peasant marketplaces
   C. prevent local governments from interfering with the market
   D. give sellers increased power over buyers

True / False Questions

1. All societies practice reciprocity.

2. Most anthropologists classify forms of exchange into the following three types: reciprocity, redistribution and bartering.

3. All societies practice market exchange.

4. The Trobriand Islanders practice *wasi* which is a form of balanced reciprocity.

5. The !Kung insult the meat because they have to give it to the Big Man.

6. The Maring pig feast is a good example of how balanced reciprocity helps to create and sustain political alliances.

7. In many contexts, the form of exchange that exists between two individuals varies with the social distance between them.

8. In negative reciprocity, both parties to the transaction seek the greatest gain for themselves.

9. Examples of reciprocity are taxes and tributes.

10. Money is really quite a simple concept.

11. The market form of exchange requires an object used as a form of exchange, a rate at which goods and services are exchanged and some kind of government to enforce the system.

12. When money serves as a generalized medium of exchange, it can be used to acquire only certain kinds of goods and services.

13. Some cultures use money to purchase only a few categories of goods. Anthropologists call this money, *subsistence sphere money*.

14. The Tiv of Nigeria used metal rods to buy cattle or slaves but they rarely used metal rods to buy crops or chickens.

15. Living in an economy in which the market organizes economic behavior costs individuals and society nothing.

16. Some form of money or currency is found in all societies.

17. Peasant marketplaces have more similarities than they have differences with modern shopping malls and department stores.

18. One reason for the expansion of global markets is the cost of labor, why pay an American garment worker $10 per hour when a Mexican worker will do the same work for $2 per hour?

19 The "impersonality of the marketplace" is expressed by the saying, "one person's money is as green as anyone else's".

20. The "special customer" relationships in the Philippines has greatly increased the profits as well as the risks of market vendors.

Multiple Choice Answers

1.	B	(p. 147)		16.	A	(p. 154)
2.	B	(p. 148)		17.	D	(p. 154-155)
3.	A	(p. 148)		18.	B	(p. 155)
4.	C	(p. 148)		19.	C	(p. 155)
5.	D	(p. 149)		20.	D	(p. 155)
6.	D	(p. 149)		21.	E	(p. 156)
7.	A	(p. 149)		22.	D	(p. 156-157)
8.	B	(p.150)		23.	D	(p. 157)
9.	B	(p. 150)		24.	D	(p. 158)
10.	B	(p. 150)		25.	C	(p. 158-159)
11.	A	(p. 151)		26.	B	(p. 162)
12.	D	(p. 153)		27.	C	(p. 160)
13.	A	(p. 153)		28.	D	(p. 160)
14.	C	(p. 154)		29.	C	(p. 160-161)
15.	D	(p. 154)		30.	A	(p. 162)

True / False Answers

1.	T	(p. 148)		11.	F	(p. 155)
2.	F	(p. 148)		12.	F	(p. 157)
3.	F	(p. 148)		13.	F	(p. 157)
4.	T	(p. 150)		14.	T	(p. 156)
5.	F	(p. 151)		15.	T	(p. 158)
6.	T	(p. 153)		16.	F	(p. 157)
7.	T	(p. 153)		17.	F	(p. 159)
8.	T	(p. 153)		18.	T	(p. 160)
9.	F	(p. 154)		19.	T	(p. 162)
10.	F	(p.155)		20.	F	(p. 162)

Chapter 9

MARRIAGE, FAMILY, AND RESIDENCE

Multiple Choice Questions

1. A social group formed on the basis of kin relationship between its members is called a:

    A. household
    B. kin group
    C. nuclear family
    D. extended family

2. A domestic group, or people who live in the same place and share assets and certain responsibilities is called a:

    A. household
    B. kin group
    C. nuclear family
    D. extended family

3. Formulating a cross-culturally valid definition of marriage is difficult because:

    A. in many societies, such as those of Melanesia and parts of Southeast Asia, men and women do not generally share the same house
    B. in some societies, such as among the Nuer of the southern Sudan, it is possible for women to "marry" other women by paying bridewealth for them (thus allowing them to claim any children the latter bear)
    C. in some societies, as among the Nayar of southern India, husbands and wives are not responsible for the enculturation of children
    D. all of the above are reasons why it is difficult to formulate a single definition of marriage

4. The function of marriage is to:

    A. form social bonds that provide for the material needs, social support and enculturation of children
    B. define the rights and obligations a couple have toward each other and toward other people
    C. create new relationships between families and other kinds of kin groups
    D. all of the above

5. In which culture did an adult woman remain with her own kin and accept male lovers, whose only obligation was to pay "birth fees"?

    A. Nayar of southern India
    B. Yanomamo
    C. Nuer of the Sudan
    D. Tibetans, in the Himalayas

6.   The Nayar:

   A. had nuclear families
   B. were a caste whose men specialized in farming
   C. restricted their women to have sexual activity only with men of their own or a
       higher subcaste
   D. had a marriage system similar to our own

7.   In one culture, elderly women marry younger men and older men marry young
       women or even little girls. This unusual marriage pattern used to exist among the:

   A. Irish
   B. Chinese
   C. Swazi of Africa
   D. Tiwi of Australia

8.   The set of rules prohibiting marriage within his/her group is called:

   A. endogamy
   B. a caste
   C. exogamy
   D. polyandry

9.   Marriage rules that require people to marry within their own social group (such as
       within their own race or caste) are known as:

   A. exogamous rules
   B. incest taboos
   C. endogamous rules
   D. polygynous rules

10.   An example of an endogamous group is:

   A. orthodox Jews
   B. the cast system in traditional Hindu India
   C. noble classes in many ancient civilizations
   D. all of the above

11.   A marriage in which one woman has multiple husbands:

   A. is not allowed anywhere in the world
   B. is called polyandry
   C. is called polygyny
   D. is called group marriage

12.   Polygyny:

   A. is the most common form of plural marriage
   B. is less common than polyandry
   C. is not as popular as monogamy
   D. means marriage of one woman to multiple men

13. Which nineteenth century community practiced a form of group marriage?

A. Tibetan Buddhists
B. Tiwi animists
C. Oneida (New York) Christians
D. Iranian Muslims

14. Which of the following statements about polyandry is true?

A. It exists in only about a dozen societies
B. Has the advantage of preserving the family property
C. allows the wife to have a less strenuous life and a higher standard of living
D. all of the above

15. When a woman is married to a group of brothers at the same time, the marriage form is:

A. sororal polygyny
B. levirate
C. fraternal polyandry
D. serial monogamy

16. A marriage in which one man marries women who are sisters is called:

A. the levirate
B. fraternal polygamy
C. sororal polygyny
D. fraternal polygyny

17. One way to reduce rivalry among co-wives in polygynous marriages is:

A. for a man to marry friends
B. for all the wives to share one household
C. for the man to have a favorite wife
D. none of the above

18. The Yanomamo of South America:

A. formed marriage alliances for trading purposes with non-Yanomamo peoples living at their borders
B. formed marriage alliances between villages for political purposes
C. had endogamous groups and therefore made no marriage alliances
D. made no marriage alliances because they viewed individuals outside their kin groups as enemies

19. Among some peoples, when a woman dies, her sister becomes the new wife of the surviving husband. This is known as:

   A. brideservice
   B. the patrilocally extended household
   C. the sororate
   D. the incest taboo

20. Marital exchanges in North America differ from those in many other societies in that:

   A. we give gifts to the couple and others only to the groom
   B. the gifts we give are paltry in value compared to what is exchanged elsewhere
   C. we give gifts to help the couple begin a new household rather than to establish an alliance between the families of bride and groom
   D. we give elaborate gifts so that the respective families can show off their wealth to one another, and others give gifts of a more practical nature

21. When a !Kung or Yanomamo man marries a woman, he stays with her parent's band for a number of years, during which he hunts for them. This marital exchange form is called:

   A. brideservice
   B. dowry
   C. bridewealth
   D. the levirate

22. The type of marital exchange where the families of a woman transfer a portion of their wealth or property to their daughter and her husband is called:

   A. dowry
   B. bridewealth
   C. gift exchange
   D. bride bestowal payments

23. Which marital exchange custom requires a man and his relatives to transfer valuable objects (livestock, money) to the wife's family?

   A. dowry
   B. brideservice
   C. bridewealth
   D. levirate

24. A Yanomamo son-in-law who hunts with his wife's parents is:

   A. paying off his bridewealth
   B. doing brideservice
   C. just being nice
   D. doing penance for fathering an illegitimate child

25. If important property is owned by women and daughters inherit property from their mothers, then the postmarital residence pattern is most likely to be:

A. matrilocal
B. bilocal
C. neolocal
D. patrilocal

26. After marriage, if a set of brothers continue to live in or near the house of their father and bring their wives to live together in this household, the household form that results is:

A. bilocally extended
B. patrilocally extended
C. matrilocally extended
D. neolocally extended

27. Which household/family form results when most young couples establish their own residence away from either set of parents?

A. matrilocally extended
B. bilocally extended
C. patrilocally extended
D. nuclear family

28. In which postmarital residence pattern do most couples live with the husband's maternal uncle?

A. patrilocal
B. matrilocal
C. neolocal
D. avunculocal

29. When women control or own important resources the postmarital residence pattern is probably:

A. neolocal
B. matrilocal
C. patrilocal
D. bilocal

True / False Questions

1. A person's relatives through marriage are her or his consanguines.

2. Organized, cooperative groups formed on the basis of kinship relations are called extended families.

3. In traditional China and Japan a man and woman often married before they had even met.

4. Marriage, in come form, is universal in human societies.

5. In no society are the members of the same nuclear family allowed to have sex, marry, and produce children.

6. Marriage among the Nayar is unusual because it doesn't exist under the definition of marriage used in the book.

7. Most Americans think the choice of whom to marry is largely a *private* matter between the couple. In many other cultures, marriage serves different functions and is more likely to be an issue of great concern between the *families* of the couple.

8. Tiwi marriage includes a cultural requirement that all females be married virtually all their lives.

9. Exogamous rules require an individual to marry within his or her family or other kin group.

10. Most societies allow a man to marry more than one woman.

11. The Oneida community, a conservative Christian utopian community, practiced group marriage and only allowed the most physically and mentally fit members to have children.

12. While most cultures allow polgynous marriage, only a minority of men in these societies actually have more than one wife.

13. Polyandry, the marriage of one woman simultaneously to two or more men is a documented practice in about a dozen societies.

14. For the Yanomamo, marriage was a way to create bonds and establish political relations between villages.

15. The practice of a widow marrying her dead husband's close kinsman is called the sororate.

16. As anthropologists use the term, *dowry* refers to the wealth a man gives a woman's family upon their marriage.

17. Brideservice is the widespread custom that requires a man and his relatives to transfer wealth to the relatives of the bride.

18. Postmarital residence patterns are important partly because they affect the kinds of families and household groups that exist in a community.

19. The symbol for a male in a kinship diagram is a circle.

20. The postmarital residence pattern of Americans is cross-culturally rare.

Multiple Choice Answers

1.	B	(p. 167)	16.	C	(p. 175)
2.	A	(p. 167)	17.	D	(p. 175)
3.	D	(p. 167-168)	18.	B	(p. 176)
4.	D	(p. 168-169)	19.	C	(p. 177)
5.	A	(p. 169)	20.	C	(p. 177)
6.	C	(p. 169-170)	21.	A	(p. 178)
7.	D	(p. 170)	22.	A	(p. 178)
8.	C	(p. 171)	23.	C	(p. 178)
9.	C	(p. 172)	24.	B	(p. 178)
10.	A	(p. 172)	25.	A	(p. 179)
11.	B	(p. 172)	26.	B	(p. 179)
12.	A	(p. 172)	27.	D	(p. 179)
13.	C	(p. 173)	28.	D	(p. 179)
14.	D	(p. 174-175)	29.	B	(p. 180)
15.	C	(p. 175)			

True / False Answers

1.	F	(p. 166)	11.	T	(p. 173)
2.	F	(p. 166)	12.	T	(p. 173)
3.	T	(p. 167)	13.	T	(p. 175)
4.	T	(p. 168)	14.	T	(p. 176)
5.	T	(p. 169)	15.	F	(p. 177)
6.	T	(p. 169-170)	16.	F	(p. 178)
7.	T	(p. 171)	17.	F	(p. 178)
8.	T	(p. 171)	18.	T	(p. 179)
9.	F	(p. 171)	19.	F	(p. 179)
10.	T	(p. 172)	20.	T	(p. 180)

Chapter 10

KINSHIP AND DESCENT

Multiple Choice Questions

1. The kinship systems of most preindustrial societies are very important because:

    A. kinship groups and relationships usually serve many functions (they are highly "multifunctional") in these societies
    B. land and other property is often owned by lineages, clans or other kin groups in these societies
    C. most important social relationships are based on kinship, unlike in industrial societies
    D. all of the above are reasons why kinship is so important in most preindustrial cultures

2. In cultures where people trace their primary kinship relationships through their *fathers,* the descent form is called:

    A. bilateral
    B. patrilineal
    C. matrilineal
    D. none of the above

3. A culture that emphasizes either the maternal or the paternal relatives but not both is called:

    A. matrilineal
    B. patrilineal
    C. unilineal
    D. bilateral

4. Patrilineal descent:

    A. is not as common as matrilineal descent
    B. traces kin connections to the ancestors and relatives of their fathers
    C. places more importance on a person's mother's relatives
    D. none of the above

5. Matrilineal descent:

    A. is more common than patrilineal descent
    B. is a system found among the Hopi
    C. is found primarily among foragers
    D. all of the above

6.   Matrilineal:

   A. kin include the children of your mother's son
   B. means "rule by women"
   C. kin include the daughters of your mother's mother
   D. descent is more common than patrilineal descent

7.   A group of relatives who are related through *only one sex* is called:

   A. a unilineal descent group
   B. a nuclear family
   C. a cognatic descent group
   D. a bilateral descent group

8.   In matrilineal descent systems:

   A. men are not counted as relatives
   B. only matrilateral parallel cousins are allowed to marry one another
   C. men never own property
   D. none of the above

9.   Your mother's sisters' children and your father's brothers' children are your:

   A. parallel cousins
   B. cross cousins
   C. patrilineal kin
   D. matrilineal kin

10.   From "largest" (most inclusive) to "smallest" (least inclusive), what is the correct order of the following kinds of kin groups?

   A. clan-lineage-extended family-nuclear family
   B. nuclear family-lineage-extended family-clan
   C. lineage-extended family-clan-nuclear family
   D. an-extended family-lineage-nuclear family

11.   Which kind of kin group is likely to be *totemic*?

   A. extended family
   B. lineage
   C. clan
   D. nuclear family

12.   Clans:

   A. are usually exogamous
   B. can include members who are descended from a common male ancestor
   C. are usually among the most significant economic, social, and political units in the society
   D. all of the above

13. Which culture has patrilineal lineages ("patrilineages") and clans?

   A. Iban
   B. Tikopia
   C. Samoan
   D. American

14. Tikopians:

   A. have clans associated with a major crop
   B. live in Micronesia and are matrilineal
   C. are patrilineal with cognatic descent
   D. bestow titles on men called "matai"

15. The Hopi are a matrilineal people. Which of these statements applies to them?

   A. "Clan mothers" have important ritual responsibilities.
   B. A husband usually moves into the household of his wife and her sisters.
   C. Fathers seldom punish their own children, since fathers and children are in different
       descent groups.
   D. All of the above statements apply to the Hopi.

16. The "real" home of a Hopi husband is:

   A. with his mother's extended family
   B. with his wife in a patrilocally extended household
   C. with his sisters and their husbands
   D. with his matai's 'aiga

17. The range of individual choice about group membership is much wider among cultures
    that practice:

   A. cognatic descent
   B. unilineal descent
   C. patrilineal descent
   D. matrilineal descent

18. The "kindred" (an "ego-focused" group) is most important in societies with which form
    of kinship?

   A. patrilineal
   B. matrilineal
   C. bilateral
   D. the kindred is likely to be equally important in all of the above kinship systems

19. Most matrilineal cultures:

    A. are foragers
    B. are pastoralists
    C. are "primitive hordes"
    D. none of the above

20. Bilateral kindreds are:

    A. ego-focused
    B. characteristic of North American kinship
    C. only identical for siblings
    D. all of the above

21. About 60% of all foraging cultures are:

    A. patrilineal
    B. cognatic or bilateral
    C. matrilineal
    D. the nuclear family

22. According to one hypothesis, nomadic herding and patrilineal descent are associated because:

    A. livestock are most often owned and managed by men
    B. a group of brothers often combine their animals into a single herd
    C. inheritance of animals typically passes from fathers to sons
    D. all of the above

23. Among most hunters and gatherers, bands need to have access to many territories, so their members need to be flexible in choosing which relatives to associate with. Which form of kinship allows them the greatest amount of choice?

    A. matrilineal kinship
    B. bilateral or cognatic kinship
    C. patrilineal kinship
    D. any unilineal form of kinship

24. Matrilineal descent most often occurs among people who have which form of adaptation?

    A. foraging
    B. horticulture
    C. intensive agriculture
    D. pastoralism

25. The terminological system used by most North Americans is called

A. Eskimo
B. Hawaiian
C. Omaha
D. Iroquois

26. The kinship terminology system with the fewest terms is the:

A. Eskimo
B. Hawaiian
C. Iroquois
D. Omaha

27. The kinship system that distinguishes between parallel cousins and cross cousins is:

A. Eskimo
B. Hawaiian
C. Iroquois
D. Hopi

28. Which terminological system is most often associated with patrilineal descent?

A. Eskimo
B. Hawaiian
C. Omaha
D. Iroquois

29. About 40 percent of societies that use the Hawaiian classification are:

A. cognatic
B. unilineal
C. matrilineal
D. bilateral

True / False Questions

1. In North America, most people believe they are related equally to the families of both their mothers and their fathers.

2. There are kin systems in which sons-in-law are not supposed to speak directly to their mothers-in-law.

3. Surprisingly, there are societies that pay almost no attention to how people are biologically related.

4. The term "aunt" is a natural and universal category of kinship.

5. If you lived in a patrilineal society, your relatives through your mother would probably be just as important as your relatives through your father.

6. There are about three times as many patrilineal as matrilineal cultures.

7. People who trace their descent through males from a common male ancestor belong to a matrilineal descent group.

8. Cross cousins include your mother's sisters' children and your father's brothers' children.

9. Most clans are symbolically identified with supernatural powers.

10. Tikopians have unilineal descent and are patrilineal.

11. In the Hopi culture, the fathers are the main disciplinarians of the children.

12. Avunculocal postmarital residence is associated with the matrilineal form of descent.

13. Individual choice in joining a group is most important in cognatic systems.

14. About three-fourths of pastoral societies have matrilineal descent.

15. The descent system of most horticultural peoples is bilateral.

16. Comparative research on the forms of kinship and the kin terminologies found among diverse peoples shows that there is no relationship between the "forms" and the "terminologies."

17. The easiest kinship terminology for English speakers to understand is the Hawaiian.

18. Only about 10% of all Iroquois terminologies occur in unilineal descent forms.

19. More than 90% of all cultures that use the Omaha terminological system are patrilineal.

20. The ideas people have about how they are related to one another are strongly influenced by how the descent form of their society sorts people into groups and establishes relationships between kinfolk.

Multiple Choice Answers

1.	D	(p. 187)	16.	A	(p. 194)
2.	B	(p. 189)	17.	A	(p. 196-197)
3.	C	(p. 189)	18.	C	(p. 198)
4.	B	(p. 189)	19.	D	(p. 199)
5.	B	(p. 189)	20.	D	(p. 198)
6.	C	(p. 190)	21.	B	(p. 199)
7.	A	(p. 191)	22.	D	(p. 199)
8.	D	(p. 191)	23.	B	(p. 199)
9.	A	(p. 191)	24.	B	(p. 199)
10.	A	(p. 192)	25.	A	(p. 201)
11.	C	(p. 192)	26.	B	(p. 201)
12.	D	(p. 192)	27.	C	(p. 201)
13.	B	(p. 193)	28.	D	(p. 202)
14.	A	(p. 194)	29.	B	(p. 204)
15.	D	(p. 194)			

True / False Answers

1.	T	(p. 187)	11.	F	(p. 195)
2.	T	(p. 187)	12.	T	(p. 196)
3.	F	(p. 188)	13.	T	(p. 196-197)
4.	F	(page 188)	14.	F	(p. 199)
5.	F	(p. 189)	15.	F	(p. 199)
6.	T	(p. 189)	16.	F	(p. 200)
7.	F	(p. 189)	17.	F	(p. 201)
8.	F	(p. 191)	18.	F	(p. 204)
9.	T	(p. 192)	19.	T	(p. 205)
10.	T	(p. 193)	20.	T	(p. 206)

Chapter 11

GENDER IN COMPARATIVE PERSPECTIVE

Multiple Choice Questions

1. A person's sex:

    A. is determined by biological inheritance
    B. is not culturally defined
    C. is not the same as their gender
    D. all of the above

2. Which culture constructs gender differences partly on the basis of the quantity of a substance called *nu* that people are believed to carry in their bodies?

    A. the Hopi
    B. the Hua
    C. the Iroquois
    D. the Eurasians

3. In the Hua culture, the figapa include the following kinds of people:

    A. children of both sexes who have recently been in contact with their mother
    B. women in their child-bearing years
    C. elderly men
    D. all of the above

4. In the Hua culture, the kakora include the following kinds of people:

    A. males in their early teens through the prime years who have been initiated
    B. postmenopausal women with more than two children
    C. both A and B
    D. neither A or B

5. In Hua society, post-menopausal women often play a role in men's house rituals because:

    A. their position as matriarchs ensures their authority over their sons
    B. they are cherished for the wisdom their age brings
    C. a life of childbirth and menstruation are believed to have purged them of most feminine substances
    D. they are believed to have special supernatural powers

6. Gender crossing and multiple gender identities were institutionalized among:

    A. actually, there are no human societies in which cultural norms allow a man to assume roles usually held by women
    B. the Kofyar of Nigeria
    C. many Native American peoples
    D. all human societies allow gender crossing and multiple identities

7.	Multiple gender identities, according to some anthropologists, include:

A.	man-woman and woman-man genders
B.	biological mutations of sex chromosomes
C.	hermaphrodites
D.	"neuters"

8.	Which feature was not commonly associated with cross-gendered persons among many Native American peoples?

A.	tranvestism
B.	special spiritual powers
C.	stigma and ostracism
D.	cross gender work roles

9.	Most anthropologists use the term *berdache* to refer to:

A.	Native American women who hunted and went to war
B.	a man-woman
C.	a post-menopausal woman
D.	none of the above

10.	The sexual division of labor:

A.	is changing in modern North America
B.	is a cultural universal
C.	of man the breadwinner and woman the homemaker is not a cultural universal
D.	all of the above

11.	Comparative research shows that which task is *about equally likely* to be performed by women and men?

A.	gathering shellfish and wild plants
B.	planting, tending, and harvesting crops
C.	clearing new land and preparing the soil for planting
D.	fishing and trapping of animals

12.	 Among most societies, the kinds of tasks done predominantly or exclusively by males are:

A.	gathering fuel
B.	gathering shellfish
C.	tending small animals
D.	none of the above

13.   Which task do men almost always perform?

A. making pottery
B. hunting
C. planting crops
D. gathering fuel

14.   Which task is not sex-specific?

A. preparing skins
B. tending small animals
C. wood working
D. hunting

15.   Which of the following hypotheses help account for the patterns of sexual division of labor?

A. strength
B. maintaining female fertility
C. women's role in nursing infants and young children
D. all of the above

16.   Among the Agta peoples of the Philippines:

A. men care for the children
B. women often hunt, sometimes carrying their infants on their backs
C. transvestism was common
D. all of the above

17.   Many of the tasks done by women in preindustrial cultures are repetitive, easily interruptible, and performed close to home. Which hypothesis explains the sexual division of labor by these characteristics?

A. the child-care-compatibility hypothesis
B. the strength hypothesis
C. the female domesticity hypothesis
D. the fertility maintenance hypothesis

18.   Women are least likely to be directly involved in farm work in which adaptation?

A. hunting and gathering
B. intensive agriculture
C. horticulture
D. slash and burn (shifting cultivation)

19. Which of the following is a component of gender stratification:

    A. the social roles men and women perform.
    B. the cultural value attached to women's and men's contributions to their families
    C. access to positions of power and influence.
    D. all of the above
    E. none of the above

20. The Kofyar of Nigeria:
    A. illustrate the general pattern that women are less involved in agriculture as it becomes more intensive
    B. are an example of Eurocentric bias
    C. are unusual in their sexual division of labor
    D. are highly "gender stratified" because of matrilineality

21. In societies where women have little independence outside the domestic context:

    A. they may have great autonomy managing the household as in Andalusia
    B. they may also not be allowed to own much property as in traditional China and Japan
    C. they may be socially and even legally subordinate to their fathers and husbands as in traditional China and Japan
    D. all of the above

22. Matriarchy:

    A. existed among matrilineal peoples
    B. existed among Amazons
    C. both A and B
    D. neither A or B

23. Some modern anthropologists claim that reports on women's status by early ethnographers were inaccurate because:

    A. early fieldworkers were mostly males, who had an androcentric (male) bias
    B. early fieldworkers were highly ethnocentric and had a Eurocentric (Western) bias
    C. male fieldworkers were uninterested in women's lives and had little access to female points of view in the cultures they studied
    D. all of the above are reasons for why early ethnographies may be misleading on the topic of women's status

24. Strong sexual asymmetry in status exists:

    A. in roles of political authority
    B. in matriarchies
    C. in the Iroquois
    D. all of the above

25. Which people are commonly cited as exemplars of female-male equality?

A. Iroquois
B. Kofyar
C. Hua
D. Chinese

26. Among the Iroquois:

A. women had lower status than men
B. beaver were trapped for pelts
C. both men and women went to war
D. none of the above

27. Which of the following is a determinant of a woman's status?

A. her role in production
B. ownership of productive resources
C. descent and postmarital residence
D. All of the above

28. A society where women's labor is critical for success in hunting and where the male-female equality is nearly equal is:

A. Chinese
B. BaMbuti
C. Cheyenne of the Great Plains
D. Yoruba of Nigeria

29. In America:

A. the presence of young children keeps most women from entering the workforce
B. it has become difficult for families to have an acceptable standard of living with one income
C. many women have failed to gain economic independence from men.
D. All of the above

30. Anthropological research on women's status provides women with

A. hope and a warning for greater sexual equality in industrial societies
B. little hope of sexual equality because industrial societies never change
C. little hope of sexual equality because industrial societies are not matrilineal
D. little hope of sexual equality because women have little access to money and wealth

True / False Questions

1.   One's sex, according to anthropologists, is determined culturally, not biologically.

2.   Among the Hua of New Guinea, elderly men are "like women."

3.   Some contemporary anthropologists argue that many societies have more than two genders.

4.   Among the Cheyenne of the Great Plains, men-women and women-men were believed to possess powerful love medicines.

5.   One of the main general patterns shown by comparative studies is that in almost all societies men are the "breadwinners" and women are the "homemakers".

6.   The physical differences between adult women and men are irrelevant for explaining the sexual division of labor. There are no patterns, and what sex performs which task depends entirely on the culture.

7.   The strength hypothesis explains why males rather than females predominate in trapping, butchering, and working with fibers.

8.   There are no known societies in which women hunt.

9.   Women usually contribute much more agricultural labor than men in intensive agricultural systems.

10.   One possible explanation for the female specific tasks of gardening, weaving and preparing plant food is that these tasks can be combined with child care.

11.   Women perform most of the garden labor in horticultural societies.

12.   Ninety percent of all intensive agriculturalists subsist mainly from cereal crops, such as rice, wheat, corn, barley and millet.

13.   The status of women in traditional China, Japan, and India often worsened as the women became older.

14.   Anthropological field research on human cultures has demonstrated that there are only two known matriarchical societies: the Iroquois and the Amazons.

15.   All anthropologists agree that women are *universally* subordinate to men; only the *degree* of male dominance varies cross-culturally.

16.   So far as anthropologists have discovered, there are no societies in which women rather than men are the culturally preferred occupants of main political offices.

17.   Iroquois women were not subordinate to men.

18.   Women enjoy more freedom from male authority in societies in which they control productive resources.

19.   Women in matrilineal and matrilocal societies tend to suffer from male dominance.

20.   There is usually less gender stratification in matrilocal, matrilineal societies than in others.

Multiple Choice Answers

1.	D	(p. 209)	16.	B	(p. 220)
2.	B	(p. 210-211)	17.	A	(p. 221)
3.	D	(p. 210-211)	18.	B	(p. 222)
4.	C	(p. 211)	19.	D	(p. 224)
5.	C	(p. 211)	20.	C	(p. 224)
6.	C	(p. 213)	21.	D	(p. 225)
7.	A	(p. 213)	22.	D	(p. 225)
8.	C	(p. 214-215)	23.	D	(p. 226)
9.	B	(p. 214)	24.	A	(p. 226)
10.	D	(p. 216-217)	25.	A	(p. 226)
11.	B	(p. 219)	26.	D	(p. 226-227)
12.	D	(p. 218)	27.	D	(p. 227-230)
13.	B	(p. 219)	28.	B	(p. 228)
14.	A	(p. 218-219)	29.	B	(p. 229)
15.	B	(p. 220)	30.	A	(p. 230)

True / False Answers

1.	F	(p. 209)	11.	T	(p. 221)
2.	T	(p. 210-211)	12.	T	(p. 222)
3.	T	(p. 213)	13.	F	(p. 225)
4.	T	(p. 215)	14.	F	(p. 225)
5.	F	(p. 217)	15.	F	(225-226)
6.	F	(p. 218)	16.	T	(p. 226)
7.	F	(p. 220)	17.	T	(p. 226)
8.	F	(p. 220)	18.	T	(p. 229)
9.	F	(p. 222-223)	19.	F	(p. 230)
10.	T	(p. 221)	20.	T	(p. 231)

Chapter 12

THE ORGANIZATION OF POLITICAL LIFE

Multiple Choice Questions

1. Which of the following is true?

    A. some societies do not have any form of political system
    B. leadership in chiefdoms is vested in "big men"
    C. the boundary of a polity corresponds with its cultural boundary
    D. none of the above

2. Which of the following is one of the four basic forms of political organization mentioned in the text?

    A. state
    B. band
    C. chiefdom
    D. all of the above

3. Big man leadership is characteristic of:

    A. bands
    B. tribes
    C. chiefdoms
    D. states

4. Which of the following are characteristics of bands:

    A. they consist of a number of families living together
    B. they have sodalities that unite them
    C. they are frequently found among peoples with foraging economies
    D. A and B only
    E. A and C only

5. The Comanche of the Great Plains:

    A. hunted bison under the leadership of a hereditary chief
    B. were a horticultural tribe that cooperated because of warfare
    C. had chiefdoms with a formalized and centralized political system
    D. none of the above

6. Which of the following statements about the Comanche is true?

    A. decisions were arrived at by consensus
    B. disagreement could result in changes in status in the band
    C. the "peace chief" was chosen from the most aggressive men
    D. all of the above

7. Sodalities are characteristic of:

   A. bands
   B. tribes
   C. chiefdoms
   D. states

8. Sodalities may be based on:

   A. kingroups
   B. an age set
   C. warrior societies
   D. all of the above

9. The Cheyenne of the Great Plains:

   A. were divided into ten nomadic villages, which averaged between 300 and 350 persons
   B. came together as a tribe every summer
   C. was politically controlled by the council of Forty-Four and the warrior societies
   D. all of the above

10. Which of the following is a characteristic of a chiefdom:

    A. has a formalized and centralized political system
    B. has a ranked or stratified society
    C. Governed by decree, not consensus
    D. all of the above

11. What kind of political organization did the Tahitians have?

    A. tribe
    B. band
    C. state
    D. chiefdom

12. Centralized political leadership with a formal leader with authority over his or her people are characteristics of:

    A. tribes
    B. chiefdoms
    C. states
    D. B and C
    E. all of the above

13. Centralized leadership with formal full authority and a supporting bureaucracy are characteristics of a:

A. band
B. tribe
C. chiefdom
D. state

14. Bureaucracies are characteristic of:

A. bands
B. tribes
C. chiefdoms
D. states

15. Which of the following are a level of the state:

A. ruling elite
B. bureaucracy
C. populace
D. all of the above

16. The Inca Empire of ancient Peru:

A. had a 9,500 mile highway with no wheeled vehicles for transporting goods
B. could mobilize an army of tens of thousands of soldiers
C. had no writing system for communication
D. all of the above

17. Which of the following was a role of the Sapa Inca:

A. control a multiethnic empire of between 6 and 12 million subjects
B. mobilize and supply armies numbering in the tens of thousands
C. have absolute authority over and control of all the people of the Inca empire
D. all of the above

18. Social control takes many forms such as:

A. Gossip
B. legal action
C. withdrawal of economic support
D. a and b
E. all of the above

19. Redress among the Comanche for wife-stealing is an example of:

A. the mediator form of self-help systems
B. the familial form of self-help systems
C. an incipient court system
D. capital punishment

20. The Jivaro:

    A. allows only a life for a life if the guilty party is also Jivaro
    B. believe most deaths are the result of physical violence, sorcery, or avenging spirits
    C. make a strong distinction between a feud and a war
    D. all of the above

21. The model used in judging cases in courts of mediation is called a:

    22. reasonable-person model
    23. social norm model
    24. legal sanction model
    25. none of the above

22. Unlike self-help legal systems, in court systems:

    A. authority resides with the court, not the victim
    B. the court has the authority to hear disputes, decide cases and impose sanctions
    C. can only exist in societies with centralized formal political leadership
    D. all of the above

23. One characteristic of courts of mediation is:

    A. arbitrariness because the judges had no codified laws to follow
    B. the use of a mediator such as among the Nuer
    C. the attempt to restore harmonious relations between the parties involved
    D. the use of harsh sanctions for those who have broken the peace

24. Among the Cheyenne, murder:

    A. "polluted" the murderer and endangered the well-being of the tribe
    B. required the ritual purification of the sacred arrows
    C. included not only cold-blooded killing, but also abortion and acts that compelled others to commit suicide
    D. all of the above

25. Among the Cheyenne a person guilt of murdering another Cheyenne:

    A. has to pay a fine in horses to the victim's family
    B. is executed by the Warrior societies
    C. is banished from the tribe
    D. nothing, unless the victim's family takes action and kills them

26. A court system using mediation works only if:

    A. The judges and parties involved share the same basic norms and values
    B. that punishment is difficult to enforce
    C. the guilty party is protected from retribution by the victim's relatives
    D. all of the above

27. The Code of Hammurabi:

   A. is the earliest known set of written laws
   B. set the prices physicians could charge for operations
   C. reflects the emergence of regulatory laws
   D. all of the above

28. Which of the following is a characteristic of Courts of regulation:

   A. laws are created to protect the interests of all classes
   B. the goal is to reconcile parties to a dispute
   C. they do not require individuals to subordinate their cultural norms and values to comply with the legal system
   D. laws could become politicized to serve the ends of only some segments of the society

True / False Questions

1. Political and cultural boundaries are often the same.

2. The four basic political organizations from least to most complex are: bands, tribes, chiefdoms and states.

3. A chiefdom is an egalitarian society.

4. A big man was a band leader with influence but little or no authority.

5. Simple bands were usually no more than an extended family with informal leadership.

6. The Comanche of the southern Great Plains of the United States illustrate the nature of simple bands.

7. A Comanche band consisted of a number of families, each headed by an older male member who was "peace chief".

8. Sodalities unify geographically dispersed tribes into political units.

9. Tahiti is an example of a state-level form of political organization.

10. Tahiti had sacred chiefs who were viewed as gods on earth.

11. Unlike the two-level chiefdom system, states have three levels: 1) the ruling elite, 2) a bureaucracy and 3) the populace.

12. The Inca empire included between six and twelve million subjects speaking dozens of languages and extending 2.500 miles from modern-day Ecuador to central Chile.

13. Gossip can be a form of social control.

14. One of the most frequent Comanche offenses was "child stealing".

15. The Nuer have a leopard-skin chief who negotiates the extent of the punishment of the murderer—such as his forty head of cattle as compensation.

16. The leopard-skin chief may place a villager under arrest if they refuse to follow his judgment.

17. In cases of death by poisoning or witchcraft, the Jivaro used divination to determine the guilty party.

18. The Barotse judicial system was a good example of a court of mediation.

19. The Code of Hammurabi is the earliest known set of written laws.

20. Courts of regulation were an outgrowth of state-level polities, which evolved socially and economically distinct classes and encompassed numerous culturally distinct peoples.

Multiple Choice Answers

1.	D	(p. 234-235)		15.	D	(p. 240)
2.	D	(p. 235)		16.	D	(p. 240)
3.	A	(p. 236)		17.	D	(p. 250)
4.	E	(p. 236)		18.	E	(p. 242)
5.	D	(p. 236-237)		19.	B	(p. 243)
6.	A	(p. 237)		20.	D	(p. 245-246)
7.	B	(p. 237)		21.	A	(p. 247)
8.	D	(p. 237)		22.	D	(p. 246)
9.	D	(p. 238)		23.	C	(p. 247)
10.	D	p. 239)		24.	D	(p. 248)
11.	D	(p. 239)		25.	C	(p. 248)
12.	D	(p. 239-240)		26.	A	(p. 249)
13.	D	(p. 240)		27.	D	(p. 249)
14.	D	(p. 240)		28.	D	(p. 249-250)

True / False

1.	F	(p. 235)		11.	T	(p. 240)
2.	T	(p. 235)		12.	T	(p. 240)
3.	F	(p. 235)		13.	T	(p. 242)
4.	T	(p. 236)		14.	F	(p. 243)
5.	T	(p. 236)		15.	T	(p. 244)
6.	F	(p. 237)		16.	F	(p. 244)
7.	T	(p. 237)		17.	T	(p. 245)
8.	T	(p. 237)		18.	T	(p. 246-247)
9.	F	(p. 239)		19.	T	(p. 249)
10.	T	(p. 239)		20.	T	(p. 249)

Chapter 13

SOCIAL INEQUALITY AND STRATIFICATION

Multiple Choice Questions

1. An egalitarian society:

   A. refers to the fact that all men are created equal
   B. refers to many differences in access to rewards between families and/or kin groups
   C. means that females and males receive equal or nearly equal rewards
   D. none of the above

2. From "least" to "greatest" degree of social inequality, which is the correct order?

   A. egalitarian-stratified-ranked
   B. ranked-egalitarian-stratified
   C. egalitarian-ranked-stratified
   D. stratified-ranked-egalitarian

3. Most hunter-gatherers (foragers) are "egalitarian," largely because of:

   A. the norms in their cultures that encourage reciprocal sharing
   B. the frequent movements of their bands makes it hard to accumulate property
   C. they have many options about which territories to exploit for food
   D. all of the above contribute to the egalitarianism of most foraging peoples

4. The main difference between egalitarian and ranked societies is that in the latter:

   A. there are marked differences in wealth among the classes
   B. an individual's social rank is not influenced by his or her kinship relations
   C. there are a limited number of statuses into which only certain individuals are recruited, so not everyone has access to honored offices or titles
   D. leadership statuses are less formal and more open to all

5. A society in which there are formal titles (or offices) that give differences in prestige ("status"), but do not give large differences in wealth would be considered a _____ society.

   A. egalitarian, like the !Kung
   B. ranked, like the Tikopia
   C. class, like the United States
   D. caste, like the Hindu parts of traditional India

6. Which of the following statements about Tikopian society is false?

   A. chiefs received tribute, but also redistributed most of it on public occasions
   B. chiefs exercised authority over members of their own clans
   C. each lineage within a clan was ranked with regard to the others
   D. the nobility enriched itself at the expense of commoners

7. The lowest *varna* in India's caste system is:

   A. *Kshatriyas*
   B. Shudras
   C. Brahmins
   D. Vaishas

8. Which of these does **not** occur in caste systems, like that of traditional India?

   A. beliefs that one is born into one's caste
   B. rules against physical contact between members of different caste, due to beliefs about pollution
   C. the ability to improve one's caste ranking by hard work and ability
   D. rules that people must marry someone of their own caste.

9. The major difference between class and caste is that the latter:

   A. are endogamous groups
   B. are theoretically hereditary
   C. prevent intercaste contact
   D. all of the above

10. Which of the following is an advantage of using wealth as the primary basis of class ranking in the United States?

    A. it is more measurable than other indications of class memberships
    B. wealth is the best single indication of the overall benefits individuals and receive from their citizenship in a nation
    C. extremely high wealth is correlated with ownership of productive resources (factories, financial institutions, income-producing real estate)
    D. all of the above

11. About what amount of annual income is received by the top 5% of households in the United States?

    A. over $50,000
    B. over $82,000
    C. over $120,000
    D. over 146,000

12. Inequality in the distribution of yearly income over the past few decades in the U.S. shows that:

    A. the poor gained income
    B. the rich lost income
    C. most Americans actually gained income
    D. none of the above

13. In 1998, the wealthiest **ten percent** of American families owned about _____ % of the nation's personal wealth (net worth), whereas the remaining **ninety percent** owned about _____ % of the wealth.

   A. 12, 88
   B. 32, 68
   C. 47, 53
   D. 69, 31

14. In the year 2000, the richest fifth (top 20%) of American households earned ___ % of the income.

   A. 32
   B. 39
   C. 50
   D. 62

15. About what percentage of wealth (net worth) is owned by 90% (the poorest) of all American families?

   A. 10%
   B. 20%
   C. 30%
   D. 40%

16. Which of the following is <u>not</u> an essential ideological feature that explains inequality as desirable?

   A. the ideology must affect people's cultural beliefs
   B. the ideology must be believable to large numbers of people
   C. ruling elites must resort to armed force to enforce the law
   D. all of the above

17. In a stratified society, cultural ideas and beliefs that explain existing inequalities between people as legitimate or desirable are called

   A. values
   B. ideologies
   C. religions
   D. none of the above

18. Which stratified society believed its elite was endowed with *mana*?

   A. Hawaii
   B. Bunyoro
   C. Japan
   D. India

19. Two secular ideologies used to justify inequality in the contemporary United States are:

A. the belief that Christian values are rewarded with success and that "money isn't everything"
B. the idea that differences in wealth are natural and nothing can be done to change them
C. the idea that inequality motivates people to do their best and success is the result of hard work
D. the belief that current wealth differences are only temporary and sound economic policy will eliminate them

20. Suppose you talk to someone who says that stratification benefits the *entire society* because it ensures that the most talented and hardworking people fill the most valuable social roles. This person would be following the _____ theory of stratification and inequality.

A. secular
B. functionalist
C. egalitarian
D. conflict

21. Which of these statements about functionalist theories of inequality is true?

A. functionalist theories argue that unequal rewards recruit the most able individuals in to the most socially valuable roles
B. functionalist theories stress that talents and skills are not uniformly distributed throughout any given population
C. functionalist theories neglect the effects of inherited advantages in determining individual life chances
D. all of the above are true of functionalist theories of inequality

22. Which of the following is a criticism of the functionalist theory:

A. no one knows how much inequality is needed to motivate people
B. it is a large assumption that those who are best able to perform the most important roles are those who are recruited into them
C. in all systems of stratification there is an element of inherited wealth, prestige and power
D. All of the above

23. Suppose you argue that the government should tax the richest individuals and families and use the tax money for public education, so that the whole nation will benefit from developing the talents of people now poor. You would be implicitly following which theory of inequality?

A. conflict
B. ideological
C. functional
D. egalitarian

24. Karl Marx argued:

   A. that capitalist societies include only two fundamental classes
   B. profit is based on the exploitation of workers
   C. exploitation of the workers would disappear when they collectively owned the means of production
   D. all of the above

25. Of the following, which sums up what we have learned about stratified societies from the anthropologist's comparative perspective?

   A. the elite provide valued services for society at large
   B. the functions the elite serve are illusionary
   C. the elite serve some valuable services for the society as a whole but some are illusionary
   D. the functionalist theory of social inequality is better than the conflict theory

True / False Questions

1. Rewards are commonly divided into three categories: wealth, power and prestige.

2. Fried identified three types of inequality based on sex and age.

3. An egalitarian society means there are few differences in the rewards received by families or other kinds of kin groups within a society.

4. Egalitarian societies are at the low end of the inequality continuum.

5. One reason access to rewards is evenly distributed among foragers is that mobility makes it difficult to transport possessions and accumulate wealth.

6. Chiefs and members of the Tikopian nobility had little more wealth than anyone else.

7. Most individuals in stratified societies die in the stratum of their birth.

8. The Hindu believe that the caste into which a Hindu is born depends on the behavior of one's soul in previous incarnations.

9. In the United States, rankings based on occupational prestige match up almost perfectly with amount of money people working in those occupations make.

10. In recent years, the wealthiest 400 Americans have a "net worth" greater than the combined 1999 gross domestic product (GDP) of Canada and Argentina.

11. Since about 1970, inequality in the distribution of household income has increased.

12. The top 5% of American families earned approximately 20% of the total family income.

13. Census bureau data over the past couple of decades show that inequality in the distribution of yearly income has increased in the United States since the 1970's.

14. In the United States, everyone has the same opportunity to compete for culturally valued rewards, so there is no true social stratification.

15. To be considered an "ideology," a stratified society's dominant ideas and beliefs must originate in its religious traditions.

16. In the ancient complex chiefdoms of Hawaii the nobility was viewed as endowed with a supernatural power called *tubu*.

17. In industrial societies such as the United States, ideologies are based mainly on religion.

18. One objection to the functionalist theory is that no one knows how much inequality is needed to motivate people.

19. Karl Marx is considered the "father" of conflict theory.

20. Functionalism emphasizes the negative aspects of stratification, while conflict theory emphasizes the positive aspects.

Multiple Choice Answers

1.	D	(p. 255)	14.	C	(p. 261)
2.	C	(p. 255)	15.	C	(p. 261)
3.	D	(p. 255-256)	16.	C	(p. 262-264)
4.	C	(p. 256	17.	B	(p. 264)
5.	B	(p. 256)	18.	A	(p. 264)
6.	D	(p. 256)	19.	C	(p. 265)
7.	B	(p. 257)	20.	B	(p. 266)
8.	C	(p. 257–258)	21.	D	(p. 266-267)
9.	D	(p. 257)	22.	D	(p. 267)
10.	D	(p. 260)	23.	A	(p. 267
11.	D	(p. 260)	24.	D	(p. 267)
12.	D	(p. 260)	25.	C	(p. 268-269)
13.	D	(p. 261)			

True / False Answers

1.	T	(p. 255)	11.	T	(p. 260-261)
2.	F	(p. 255)	12.	T	(p. 260)
3.	T	(p. 255)	13.	T	(p. 260)
4.	T	(p. 255)	14.	F	(p. 262-263)
5.	T	(p. 255)	15.	F	(p. 264)
6.	T	p. 256	16.	F	(p. 264)
7.	T	(p. 257)	17.	F	(p. 265)
8.	T	(p. 258)	18.	T	(p. 266)
9.	F	(p. 260)	19.	T	(p. 267)
10.	T	(p. 260-261)	20.	F	(p. 268)

Chapter 14

RELIGION AND WORLD VIEW

Multiple Choice Questions

1. Which statement about religion is true?

    A. there are some primitive societies that have no religion
    B. all religions believe in the existence of gods
    C. people who live in complex societies are less religious than those who live in simple societies
    D. some form of religion is universal among human societies

2. The belief in spiritual beings is called:

    A. sorcery
    B. magic
    C. religion
    D. none of the above

3. The concept of mana is used to explain:

    A. why some chiefs always won battles
    B. why certain gardens produced such fine crops
    C. why people seem to encounter the dead in dreams
    D. none of the above
    E. A and B

4. Myths are:

    A. stories recited only on appropriate occasions
    B. told to pass the time
    C. told only at night
    D. help form a people's world view

5. The organized performance of behaviors intended to influence spiritual powers is called:

    A. animism
    B. mana
    C. ritual
    D. myths

6. Rituals that occur at regular and predictable time intervals are called:

    A. rites of passage
    B. calendrical rituals
    C. divination rituals
    D. crisis rituals

7. Which "theory" holds that the main function of religion is to help people understand and explain things and events in the world?

    A.   psychological theory
    B.   intellectual/cognitive theory
    C.   sociological theory
    D.   communal theory

8. According to Sir James Frazer:

    A.   magic and science are alternative world views
    B.   early cultures practiced magic and attempted to control the world by performing rites and spells
    C.   science replaced the errors of magic and religion with the knowledge of true cause and effect relationships
    D.   all of the above

9. Which approach holds that the main function of religion is to explain things and events that cannot be explained by other aspects of cultural knowledge?

    A.   psychological
    B.   intellectual/cognitive
    C.   sociological
    D.   none of the above

10. The psychological function for religion:

    A.   helps people cope psychologically with times of trouble and stress
    B.   gives people confidence according to Malinowski
    C.   helps people cope with death
    D.   all of the above

11. A scholar who argues that the main value of rituals is that they instill values and maintain social solidarity would be following the _____ theory of religion.

    A.   psychological
    B.   illusional
    C.   intellectual
    D.   sociological

12. Emile Durkheim's theory of religion stressed the idea that:

    A.   the main function of religion was to promote social solidarity
    B.   religion exists because it is socially useful
    C.   when people periodically congregate for the performance of religious rituals they are promoting social solidarity
    D.   all of the above

13. Which of the following statements about Azande witchcraft beliefs is true?

   A. if a granary collapses, witchcraft is blamed
   B. if a person is killed by the collapse of a granary, witchcraft is blamed
   C. if a person is killed by the collapse of a granary, witchcraft is blamed unless it can be shown that the victim had been there of his or her own volition
   D. if a person is killed by the collapse of a granary, witchcraft is blamed unless it can be shown that the victim was only present as a matter of coincidence

14. The Ibibio of Nigeria believe:

   A. when witches want to torture their victims they remove the victim's soul and place it in water or hang it over a fireplace or flog it in the evening
   B. witches walk around at night disguised as nocturnal animals
   C. witches are associated with the sins of bestiality, incest and necrophilia
   D. witches are motivated by their lust for food

15. If a society has powerful rulers and a specialized priesthood, its religious organization is likely to be:

   A. individualistic
   B. shamanistic
   C. communal
   D. ecclesiastical

16. The vision quest among the Native Americans of the Plains represents which kind of "cult"?

   A. individualistic
   B. shamanistic
   C. communal
      D. ecclesiastical

17. Shamanistic cults are most prominent among which people?

   A. Jivaro of Ecuador
   B. Lugbara of Uganda
   C. Azande of Sudan
   D. Trobriands of the Pacific

18. A shaman:

   A. seeks out spirits in a vision quest
   B. can be a person who uses jewelry and clothing to harm an enemy
   C. often cures sickness
   D. is an elder among the Lugbara who maintains lineage harmony by invoking ghosts

19. Spirit helpers, curing, and trances are most often associated with:

A. shamanistic cults
B. witchcraft
C. calendrical rituals
D. communal cults

20. If a people's religion includes ancestral cults, then _____ probably are important groups in their society.

A. nuclear families
B. mobile and bilateral bands
C. castes
D. lineages and/or clans

21. If a society is "complex," has powerful chiefs or rulers, and has a lot inequality, it is likely to have a religious organization that anthropologists call:

A. individualistic
B. shamanistic
C. communal
D. ecclesiastical

22. Cargo cults in Melanesia are a form of:

A. ecclesiastical cult
B. individualistic cult, since they had prophets
C. revitalization movement
D.   shamanistic cult

23. Revitalization movements are likely to occur:

A. during a time of little change
B. when people see themselves as lacking wealth and power
C. during foreign domination
D. B and C
E. All of the above

24. Peyote:

A. is a small cactus that grows in the Rio Grande valley of Texas and northern Mexico
B. produces a mild narcotic effect when eaten
C. provided meaning and moral direction to tribal life during a period of rapid and harmful change
D.   all of the above

25. Most revitalization movements:

    A.   disappear
    B.   develop into formal churches
    C.   turn into cults
   D. none of the above

True / False Questions

1. Belief in spiritual beings is called animism.

2. The religious heritage of Westerners may suggest that the earth is for us to conquer and exploit rather than to preserve and protect.

3. Not all the world's religions have rituals and symbols.

4. Crisis rituals are performed for purposes of curing, ensuring good hunting or fishing, or other events that happen unpredictably.

5. Sir James Frazer views magic, religion and science as alternative world views.

6. The belief in a life after death is an example of the psychological function of religion.

7. The idea of the sociological approach is that religion exists because of the useful effects it has on human societies.

8. A sorcerer is defined by anthropologists as one who uses rites and spells to cause supernatural forces to harm others.

9. Witchcraft and sorcery accusations often are *patterned*, meaning that persons holding roles that are likely to have built in conflicts are especially likely to accuse one another.

10. The Nyakyusa of Tanzania believe that witches are motivated by their lust for food and suck dry the udders of people's cattle and devour the internal organs of their human neighbors while they sleep.

11. In cultures with witchcraft and sorcery beliefs, innocent people are sometimes accused of harming others. Therefore, witchcraft does not perform any useful social functions.

12. Blaming one's troubles on witches is an example of the cognitive interpretation by which a society benefits from such misfortune.

13. According to one sociological interpretation, witchcraft beliefs serve as a mechanism of social control.

14. Despite decades of research, anthropologists have yet to discover any broad, general patterns that connect "kinds of religions" with "kinds of societies."

15. According to Wallace's typology of religion, ecclesiastical cults always have a medicine man or shaman.

16. Ancestral cults and totemic cults are both forms of "communal cults."

17. The Lugbara, of Uganda, believe that ancestral ghosts punish living descendents who violate Lugbara ideals of behavior toward lineage mates.

18. Totemism refers to the belief that the souls of the dead interact with their living relatives.

19. Most Christian denominations are ecclesiastical cults according to Wallace's typology.

20. People join revitalization movements to preserve their way of life or cope with changing conditions.

Multiple Choice Answers

1.	D	(p. 272)	14.	A	(p. 282)
2.	D	(p. 273)	15.	D	(p. 283)
3.	E	(p. 273)	16.	A	(p. 284)
4.	D	(p. 274)	17.	A	(p. 285)
5.	C	(p. 274)	18.	D	(p. 285)
6.	B	(p. 275)	19.	A	(p. 285)
7.	B	(p. 276)	20.	D	(p. 286)
8.	D	(p. 276)	21.	D	(p. 287)
9.	B	(p. 276-277)	22.	C	(p. 288)
10.	D	(p. 277-278)	23.	D	(p. 288)
11.	D	(p. 278-279)	24.	D	(p. 291)
12.	D	(p. 279)	25.	A	(p. 291)
13.	B	(p. 281)			

True / False Answers

1.	T	(p. 273)	11.	F	(p. 281)
2.	T	(p. 273-274)	12.	T	(p. 281)
3.	F	(p. 274)	13.	T	(p. 282)
4.	T	(p. 275)	14.	F	(p. 283)
5.	T	(p. 276)	15.	F	(p. 283-285)
6.	T	(p. 277-278)	16.	T	(p. 286)
7.	T	(p. 278)	17.	T	(p. 286)
8.	T	(p. 279)	18.	F	(p. 287)
9.	T	(p. 281)	19.	T	(p. 287-288)
10.	T	(p. 281)	20.	T	(p. 288)

Chapter 15

ART AND THE AESTHETIC

Multiple Choice Questions

1. Which of the following is true?

    A. aesthetics have clear and universal standards
    B. the fine ornamentation on Shaker furniture makes it art
    C. the Shakers said their designs came from heaven, communicated to them by angels
    D. none of the above

2. Shaker furniture:

    A. is considered art because of its ornamentation
    B. is too simple to be considered as art
    C. is too functional and utilitarian to be art
    D. none of the above

3. Art:

    A. is created when something's functional nature is modified for the purpose of making it more pleasurable to our sense
    B. can be used as a means of communication
    C. is inseparable form the aesthetic
    D. all of the above

4. The idea of "art for art's sake" is:

    A. an ancient Western expression
    B. found in every culture
    C. an artificial and unfortunate categorization of art whose sole value is aesthetic
    D. all of the above

5. Which of the following is true?

    A. Native Americans had no word for art in their languages
    B. art is not a cultural universal
    C. the word "tattoo" is Egyptian
    D. tattooing and scarification are usually associated with stratified societies

6. Which of the following is considered artistic?

    A. wearing jewelry
    B. setting the table for a fancy dinner
    C. putting in a vegetable garden
    D. all of the above

7. Which of the following is **not** true?

   A. marriageable girls among the Hopi wear their hair in a "butterfly" style
   B. noblewomen in ancient Egypt frequently wore "artificial beards"
   C. some peoples deformed the skulls of their babies by binding them
   D. some ancient Mesoamericans-Americans cut their ears off and substituted them with gold ears

8. Cranial deformation, or skull shaping is a type of:

   A. body art
   B. visual art
   C. performance art
   D. ornamental art

9. Tattoo designs in Polynesia indicate a persons:

   A. class or rank
   B. sex or gender
   C. religious role
   D. all of the above

10. Maori men who did not have tattoos were not allowed to:

    A. build canoe houses
    B. carve wood
    C. make weapons
    D. all of the above

11. The Marquesa:

    A. had the most tattoos of any people in Polynesia
    B. believed that tattoo images protected the body from spiritual harm.
    C. Tattooed their highest ranking chiefs on the soles of their feet.
    D. All of the above

12. Horizontal cuts on the foreheads of Nuer men mean that they:

    A. have completed male initiation rituals
    B. are chiefs
    C. are married
    D. have killed in battle

13. According to the Maori concept of art:

   A. through decoration, an object is transformed from the natural world to the cultural world.
   B. the act of placing designs on an object gives *korero* and thus makes it *taonga*
   C. an artist is a vehicle used by the gods to express their artistry and their genius
   D. A and B only
   E. all of the above

14. Native American art of the Northwest Coast is famous for:

   A. tattooing
   B. petroglyphs
   C. sandpaintings
   D. "totem poles"

15. Arts meant to be heard, seen, or personally performed, such as music, song, dance and theater, are forms of:

   A. body arts
   B. visual arts
   C. performance arts
   D. musical arts

16. John Fischer's study of stylistic elements in 28 different societies found that:

   A. there was too much variation within each society to make any generalizations
   B. the styles of egalitarian societies differed from those of stratified ones
   C. male artists differed greatly from female artists
   D. none of the above

17. !Kung shamans use percussion, song, and dance to:

   A. please ancestral ghosts
   B. diagnose illnesses
   C. warm up a substance called *n!um*
   D. all of the above

18. Tumbuka diver-healers of Malawi:

   A. use music and dance to heal the sick
   B. always destroy their sandpaintings when they are finished
   C. are always *berdaches*
   D. conduct male initiation ceremonies using flutes

19. In his study of dance and songs, Lomax found:

    A. differences in song styles correlated with societal complexity
    B. dance movements were formalized repetitions of the movements found in daily life
    C. the form of dance was correlated with the relative complexity of the society
    D. all of the above

20. Which of the following is true?

    A. Western art is mostly religious in its themes
    B. Classical Greek art was mostly secular
    C. Western art has become increasingly secular since about 1700
    D. in ancient Greek drama the roles of men were played by women

21. Navajo sandpaintings are created:

    A. for specific curing ceremonials held for particular patients
    B. to celebrate Navajo culture
    C. last for centuries
    D. all of the above

22. The most common cause of sickness among the Navajo:

    A. are spirits called *vimbuza*
    B. is the loss of harmony with the environment
    C. are kachina spirits called *bultos*
    D. none of the above

23. Which of the following is not a form of artistic expression?

    A. scarification
    B. music
    C. the playing of musical instruments by Shakers
    D. none of the above

24. Among the Plains Indians:

    A. the only men who produced beadwork and quillwork were men who dressed and acted like women
    B. the containers used for storage of food and clothing were made by men and were painted with representational designs
    C. tipis were made by women, but always painted by men
    D. all of the above

25. Which of the following is gender specific?

    A. playing flutes at night among the BaMbuti
    B. Navajo curing ceremonies
    C. Voudon drumming at temples
    D. incising designs on pottery among the Osage

26. Traditional Navajo art had little tourist appeal because the:

    A. pottery was too large
    B. jewelry was too heavy
    C. blankets were too thin
    D. all of the above

27. Which of the following is true:

    A. although many Hopi kachinas are female, in traditional kachina dances all dancers are men
    B. In ancient Greek drama, the roles of women were played by men
    C. Women could not perform in the English theater until the late 17th century
    D. All of the above

28. In contemporary society the use and consumption of art may be used to express our:

    A. individuality
    B. group or social identity
    C. relative social status
    D. all of the above

29. The carvings on Maori dwellings are:

    A. the same on every home in the village
    B. different for each home
    C. the marking of clan identity
    D. none of the above

30. Through art, people can express their:

    A. personal individuality
    B. group identity and ethnic affiliation
    C. social status
    D. all of the above

True / False Questions

1. The Shakers of the 19th century emphasized the qualities of simplicity and utility in everything they made, so they were not really artists.

2. Some traditional peoples have no word for art in their language.

3. Only fine arts, such as painting, sculpture, music and dance, are considered by anthropologists to be "true" art.

4. Creative artistic expressions are found in even the most mundane acts of the daily lives of all peoples.

5. Only the nobility of ancient Greece were allowed to shave their beards.

6. Tattooing was never practiced among the peoples of Europe until the eighteenth century when sailors discovered it in Polynesia and introduced it back home.

7. In the fourth century A.D. , when Christianity became the official religion of the Roman Empire, tattooing was forbidden on religious grounds.

8. Maori facial tattoos were designed by splitting the face into two areas, above and below the lower eyelid.

9. According to one interpretation, voluntary tattooing gives pain to men just as childbirth causes pain to women.

10. The visual arts of nomadic and seminomadic peoples are "less refined" than that of more settled peoples.

11. John Fischer found that in more stratified societies ornamentation was characterized by asymmetrical designs that integrated unlike elements.

12. Many peoples believe that music, song and dance are essential elements in curing ceremonies.

13. Music therapy is a new field for the treatment of various disorders.

14. Throughout most of human history, art was, for the most part, concerned with religion.

15. Navajo sand paintings are visual and sacred representations that are created, used several times in special ceremonies, and then destroyed.

16. The Koran prohibits the use of human images.

17. An important factor that distinguishes ethnic art from traditional art, is that the buyers and sellers belong to different ethnic groups.

18. In designs and colors, Navajo rugs of today are exact copies of Navajo blankets woven during the nineteenth century.

19. A boy performed the role of Juliet in the in original production of Shakespeare's play.

20. Through the production, consumption and use of art, we can express our personal identity, our group identities, and even our social status.

Multiple Choice Answers

1.	C	(p. 295)	16.	B	(p. 305)
2.	D	(p. 295)	17.	C	(p. 306)
3.	D	(p. 295-296)	18.	A	(p. 306)
4.	C	(p. 296)	19.	D	(p. 307)
5.	A	(p. 296)	20.	C	(p. 307)
6.	D	(p. 296)	21.	A	(p. 308)
7.	D	(p. 297-298)	22.	B	(p. 308)
8.	A	(p. 298)	23.	D	(p. 309)
9.	D	(p. 299)	24.	A	(p. 309)
10.	D	(p. 299)	25.	A	(p. 309)
11.	D	(p. 300)	26.	D	(p. 311)
12.	A	(p. 300)	27.	D	(p. 312)
13.	E	(p. 301)	28.	D	(p. 312)
14.	D	(p. 304)	29.	B	(p. 312)
15.	C	(p. 305)	30.	D	(p. 312)

True / False Answers

1.	F	(p. 295)	11.	T	(p. 305)
2.	T	(p. 296)	12.	T	(p. 306)
3.	F	(p. 296)	13.	F	(p. 306-307)
4.	T	(p. 296)	14.	T	(p. 307)
5.	T	(p. 297)	15.	F	(p. 308)
6.	F	(p. 299)	16.	T	(p. 309)
7.	T	(p. 299)	17.	T	(p. 310)
8.	F	(p. 299)	18.	F	(P. 311)
9.	T	(p. 300)	19.	T	(p. 312)
10.	F	(p. 301)	20.	T	(p. 312)

Chapter 16

GLOBALIZATION

Multiple Choice Questions

1. Globalization is:

    A. not just an economic issue
    B. began 500 years ago, with the voyage of Columbus
    C. impacts our political, social and cultural institutions
    D. all of the above

2. The term "Old World" applies to:

    A. Europe
    B. Africa
    C. Asia
    D. all of the above

3. Which of the following is true regarding European powers in 1500 A.D.?

    A. they were technologically superior to Asia only in naval warfare
    B. their population size was larger than Asia
    C. their armies were technologically superior to those of the Asian states
    D. they were in extensive and direct contact with China

4. Which of the following European powers was an important conqueror in the New World?

    A. Spain
    B. Portugal
    C. England
    D. all of the above

5. The Africa slave trade was directly linked to:

    A. the collapse of the native American population
    B. the development of larger sailing ships
    C. European conquest of Africa
    D. the opium trade with China

6. As early as 1619, English colonists in Virginia were:

    A. buying slaves
    B. growing corn and manioc introduced by the Portuguese
    C. using Native Americans as laborers on their farms
    D. converting Indians to Christianity

7. Portugal's chief source of wealth in its early phase of Asian colonization came from:

A. the slave trade
B. traffic in plantation products such as sugar and cocoa
C. gold, silver, and precious gems originating in Asia
D. none of the above

8. The next European power to compete for trade with Asia after the Spanish and the Portuguese was:

A. English
B. French
C. German
D. Dutch

9. Which of the following is true of the industrial revolution:

A. it escalated political revolutions in the Americas
B. it slowed the slave trade
C. reduced taxation of local peoples
D. all of the above

10. Which of the following is true about the exploitation of the native population of the Congo basin in the mid-18th century:

A. King Leopold of Belgium claimed the Congo as "Crown Lands" and organized it as the Congo Free State.
B. the labor conditions were some of the most brutal and exploitive in world history
C. Africans were forcibly conscripted to work on the plantations and in the minds.
D. all of the above

11. By end of the nineteenth century the only Asian state to fully retain its autonomy from European powers was:

A. China
B. India
C. Japan
D. Burma

12. The first non-western country to become an industrial power was:

A. China
B. India
C. Japan
D. Korea

13. In 1785 the English established a penal colony in:

A. India
B. Guam
C. Australia
D. Hawaii

14. The GATT talks tried to achieve:

A. minimum wage laws
B. environmental laws
C. "free trade" throughout the world
D. none of the above

15. According to some experts, the global economy:

A. is enriching governments at the expense of corporations
B. requires price controls and tariffs
C. is no different from global trade 500 years ago
D. requires the adoption of a Western ideology, i.e., capitalism

16. If a WTO tribunal finds against a country, the country has the option to:

A. appeal
B. pay compensation
C. have trade sanctions imposed
D. A and C only
E. B and C only

17. Before a global economy could develop, a number of changes had to occur, including

A. collapse of colonial empires
B. technological changes which lowered the shipping cost of goods.
C. communications systems which allowed for quicker communications between peoples in different countries.
D. A and B
E. B and C
F. all of the above

18. A company that has most of its employees, produces and sells most of its products or services, and generates most of its gross revenues in countries other than its "home" country is called a:

A. transnational corporation.
B. global trader
C. key corporation
D. none of the above

19. In much of the Arab world:

    A. courts of law are separate from religion
    B. Islamic banks make profits without charging interest
    C. world banks such as Citibank are still expanding their business operations in the Middle East
    D. all of the above

20. Which of the following is false?

    A. globalization is allowing the standard of living for the poor to catch up to the rest of us
    B. the richest 20% of the world's peoples now have 74 times more income than the poorest 20%
    C. the poorest people now make over a dollar a day
    D. A and C only
       E. none of the above

21. The United Nations estimates that _____ million people now live in a country other than the one in which they were born.

    A. 50
    B. 150
    C. 250
    D. 500

22. Which of the following statements about global demographic changes in recent times is false?

    A. the fastest growing cities are in non-industrialized nations
    B. great numbers of peoples from Third World nations are emigrating to the highly industrialized countries
    C. twenty-five percent of American population growth since World War II has been the result of immigration
    D. none of the above

23. One of the world's five most rapidly growing cities is in:

    A. Japan
    B. America
    C. Indonesia
    D. Europe

24. West Germany initiated a "guest-worker" program to recruit laborers from:

    A. America
    B. Africa
    C. actually they have always had strong laws against foreign immigrants
    D. none of the above

25. Giddens states in his book, *Runaway World*, that the battleground of the 21st century will pit:

    A. Christianity against Islam
    B. Fundamentalism against cosmopolitan tolerance
    C. Developed countries against undeveloped countries
    D. America against terrorists

True-False Questions

1. The term "New World" refers to Europe, Africa and Asia.

2. In A.D. 1500, Europe had a larger population size than Asia.

3. In A.D. 1500, European naval warfare was technologically superior to that of Asia.

4. The first major traders of African slaves were the Spanish and Portuguese colonies.

5. Most of the 10 million African slaves brought to the Americas came as a result of the industrial revolution.

6. The Global economy has greatly improved the standard of living of all of the world's peoples.

7. Nokia was originally a paper manufacturer.

8. It is estimated that by 2025, the population of the developed countries of the world will constitute only about one-sixth of the world's population.

9. The fastest growing cities in the world are now found in the industrialized countries of Western Europe, North America and Asia.

10. The highest birth rates in the world are found in the most economically developed countries.

11. The wealth of the richest 200 individuals in the world exceeds the annual income of over one-third the world's population.

12. Most immigrants to the U.S. today are from Asia.

13. South Africa has proportionately the greatest problem with illegal workers with an estimated 4 million illegals out of a total population of 43 million.

14. Gidden's book, *Runaway World*, predicts conflicts in the context of globalization.

15. Globalization has made the problems of one region of the world quickly become the problems of another and the problems of the Middle East have become the problems of America.

Answers for Chapter 16

Multiple Choice Answers

1.	D	(p. 318)	14.	C	(p. 328-329)
2.	D	(p. 318)	15.	D	(p. 328-330)
3.	A	(p. 318)	16.	E	(p. 329)
4.	D	(p. 319-320)	17.	F	(p. 330)
5.	A	(p. 320-321)	18.	A	(p. 334)
6.	A	(p. 321-323)	19.	B	(p. 334)
7.	D	(p. 324)	20.	D	(p. 337)
8.	D	(p. 324)	21.	B	(p. 338)
9.	A	(p. 324-325)	22.	D	(p. 338)
10.	D	(p. 326)	23.	C	(p. 338)
11.	C	(p. 326)	24.	D	(p. 338)
12.	C	(p. 326)	25.	B	(p. 341)
13.	C	(p. 327)			

True / False Answers

1.	F	(p. 318)	9.	F	(p. 336)
2.	F	(p. 318)	10.	F	(p. 336)
3.	T	(p. 318)	11.	T	(p. 337)
4.	T	(p. 320)	12.	T	(p. 339)
5.	T	(p. 325)	13.	T	(p. 340)
6.	F	(p. 328-330)	14.	T	(p. 341)
7.	T	(p. 334)	15.	T	(p. 342)
8.	T	(p. 336)			

Chapter 17

ETHNICITY AND ETHNIC CONFLICT

Multiple Choice Questions

1. A formal, named grouping of people who see themselves as sharing a common cultural-historical tradition is called:

    A. ethnic group
    B. homeland
    C. subnationality
    D. civilization

2. The situational nature of ethnic identity demonstrates:

    A. the hierarchical nesting quality of identity
    B. the trivial nature of ethnicity
    C. that only minorities are ethnic groups
    D. that it is impossible for ethnic groups to divide the social world into categories of "us" and "them"

3. Which of the following helps to define and identify an ethnic group?

    A. they all have an origin myth
    B. language and religion
    C. physical characteristics
    D. all of the above

4. Which of the following is an important attribute of an ethnic group?

    A. various ethnic boundary markers
    B. origin myth
    C. sharing the same socioeconomic class and language
    D. A and B
    E. all of the above

5. Which of the following types of characteristics may serve as ethnic boundary markers:

    A. clothing
    B. language
    C. religion
    D. physical differences
    E. all of the above

6. The kilts worn by men in Scotland are an example of:

A. the first unisex clothing
B. an adaptation to herding sheep
C. an ethnic boundary marker
D. a shortage of cloth

7. Which of the following characteristics serve to ethnically identify an individual as being Serbian instead of Croatian:

A. language
B. physical differences
C. religion
D. all of the above

8. The Tasmanians of Australia:

A. successfully assimilated into the British culture during colonization
B. has ceased to exist as a viable ethnic group
C. numbered in the tens of thousands in the 1800's
D. enjoyed a population boom in the mid 1800's

9. The process of two or more ethnic groups merging to form a new ethnic group, or an existing ethnic group splitting into two or more new ethnic groups is called:

A. ethnogenesis
B. ethnic boundary marking
C. accommodation
D. segregation

10. During the 17th, 18th and 19th centuries American Indian peoples in the United States were victims of:

A. genocide
B. relocation
C. force assimilation
D. all of the above

11. Which of the following characteristics defines a group of people as a nationality rather than a sub-national ethnic group:

A. ethnic boundary markers
B. an origin myth
C. the ideal of a separate homeland
D. all of the above

12. Ethnic groups with a feeling of homeland are:

    A. ethnic minorities
    B. subnationalities
    C. ethnic enclaves
    D. ethnic nationalities

13. The Scottish Americans are:

    A. an ethnic subnationality
    B. transnationals
    C. an artificial country
    D. ethnogenesis

14. A subnational group:

    E. sees itself as a dependent and politically subordinate subset of a nationality
    F. lacks a distinct and separate homeland
    G. lacks the rights to separate political sovereignty and self-determination
    H. all of the above

15. The Seminole:

    A. no longer exist because they have been absorbed into the South African population
    B. cannot even vote
    C. are an ethnic nationality
    D. are an example of ethnogenesis

16. The conflict in Northern Ireland in reality is between:

    A. the British and the Irish
    B. Catholics and Protestants
    C. two ethnic nationalities, the Irish and the Scotch-Irish
    D. two subnationalities, the Scottish and the Irish

17. One of the legacies of colonialism are states which have no internal ethnic cohesion, in that they encompass several hostile nationalities. These are called:

    17. artificial countries
    18. subnationalities
    19. transnational groups
    20. nationalities

18. An example of ethnic nationality is:

    A. Somalis in Ogaden
    B. Scotch-Irish of Ireland
    C. Albanians in Kosovo
    D. all of the above

19. India:

    A. is predominantly Muslim
    B. never existed before British domination
    C. is free from ethnic conflicts
    D. fought Bangladesh before becoming independent in 1967

20. The largest stateless nationality are

    21. the Tibetans
    22. the Amara Indians of South America
    23. the Kurds
    24. the Tutsi

21. One reason that the U.N. seldom recognizes separatist movements is that:

    A. they are not given any rights in the U.N. Charter
    B. most are not large enough to warrant recognition
    C. most other organizations and governments do it already
    D. none of the above

22. The physical elimination of an unwanted ethnic group or groups from particular geographical areas is called:

    A. passive assimilation
    B. segregation
    C. forced assimilation
    D. ethnic cleansing

23. Which of the following is an example of genocide:

    A. the killing of millions of Jews and Gypsies by the Germans during World War II
    B. the massacre of more than 150 Sioux at Wounded Knee, South Dakota, in 1890
    C. the massacre of thousands of Native Americans by the Guatemalan army in the late 1970s and early 1980s
    D. all of the above

24. Which of the following is <u>not</u> true regarding the collapse of the Soviet Union?

    A. it formerly included more than 100 distinct ethnic nationalities
    B. more than 80 of the smaller nationalities have yet to achieve political independence
    C. the most dangerous ethnic problems are between, not within, the new states
    D. all of the above

25. The Trail of Tears, when the Five Civilized Tribes were forced from their homes in the southeastern states to what is today Oklahoma, is an example of:

A. relocation
B. passive assimilation
C. genocide
D. forced assimilation

26. Which of the following is an example of political accommodation:

A. Canada has two main nationalities: Anglo-Canadians and French Canadians
B. Belgium has two major national groups: Flemish and Walloons
C. Spain has four main linguistic ethnic groups
D. all of the above

27. Ethnic pride rather than ethnic hostility led to the breakup of:

A. Czechoslovakia
B. Yugoslavia
C. Croatia
D. Bosnia

28. The problems between Quebec and the rest of Canada:

A. are the result of genocide
B. were resolved at the ballot box
C. show how explosive ethnic conflicts can be
D. none of the above

29. To be successful, political accommodation:

A. members of all group have to feel a social equality with members of other groups
B. no group can feel that their collective economic well-being is inhibited
C. members have to feel that their collective political rights are secure
D. all of the above

30. Two factors that most seriously threaten the political stability of multinational countries are:
A. differential rates of population growth
B. relative differences in economic development between the constituent nationalities
C. cooperation between countries and nationalities
D. A and B
E. None of the above

True / False Questions

1. Peace is more likely now in the world than ever before with the collapse of the Soviet Union and the end of the Cold War.

2. Ethnic identity is the most potent political force in the modern world.

3. A person may assume a number of different ethnic identities, depending on the situation.

4. The teaching of American history in high school is an example of an origin myth.

5. Language and religion can serve as ethnic boundary markers.

6. During the past 500 years, numerous ethnic groups have vanished.

7. The difference between nationality and subnationality is of little consequence.

8. Transnationals are members of an ethnic community located outside their country of origin and homeland.

9. Ethnic conflicts in the other regions of the world are comparable to conflicts between subnational groups within the U.S.

10. The conflict in Northern Ireland is primarily a religious war.

11. Most countries are peopled by members of a single nationality and are thus ethnically homogenous.

12. India did not exist, and never existed, as a unified country before British domination.

13. The United Nations doesn't recognize a secessionist group because doing so would be considered intervention in the affairs of a sovereign state.

14. Incidents of genocide are found in American history.

15. The statement "You have to destroy the Indian to save the man" is an example of forced assimilation.

16. During the past 100 years, the Native American population in Guatemala has decreased from about 75 percent of the total population to less than 50 percent due to genocide.

17. Samuel Huntington, sees the division between Western and Islamic civilizations as being potentially the most dangerous division of peoples in the world.

18. It was not until 1924 that U.S. citizenship and voting rights were extended to all Native Americans.

19. Creating a balanced political relationship between two or more ethnic groups, allowing each to maintain its own social identity and cultural tradition is called accommodation.

20. Two factors that most seriously threaten the political stability of multinational countries are differential rates of population growth and relative differences in economic development between the constituent nationalities.

Multiple Choice Answers

1.	A	(p. 346)	16.	C	(p. 352)
2.	A	(p. 346)	17.	A	(p. 353)
3.	D	(p. 347)	18.	B	(p. 352)
4.	D	(p. 347)	19.	B	(p. 355)
5.	E	(p. 348)	20.	B	(p. 355)
6.	C	(p. 348)	21.	D	(p. 359)
7.	C	(p. 348)	22.	D	(p. 358-359)
8.	B	(p. 349)	23.	D	(p. 359)
9.	A	(p. 349)	24.	D	(p. 360-361)
10.	D	(p. 350)	25.	A	(363)
11.	C	(p. 350)	26.	D	(p. 365)
12.	D	(p. 350)	27.	A	(368)
13.	A	(p.350)	28.	C	(p. 369)
14.	D	(p. 350)	29.	D	(p. 367-368)
15.	D	(p. 350)	30.	D	(p. 369)

True / False Answers

1.	F	(p. 345)	11.	F	(p. 353)
2.	T	(p. 346)	12.	T	(p. 355)
3.	T	(p. 326)	13.	T	(p. 359)
4.	T	(p. 347)	14.	T	(p. 359-362)
5.	T	(p. 348)	15.	T	(p. 363)
6.	T	(p. 349)	16.	F	(p. 363)
7.	F	(p. 350)	17.	T	(p. 364-365)
8.	T	(p. 351)	18.	F	(p. 364)
9.	F	(p. 351-352)	19.	T	(p. 367)
10.	F	(p. 352)	20.	T	(p. 370

Chapter 18

WORLD PROBLEMS AND THE PRACTICE OF ANTHROPOLOGY

Multiple Choice Questions

1. The application of anthropological research findings and methods to solve, or attempt to more clearly understand, contemporary global issues and problems is called:

    A. applied anthropology
    B. systematic anthropology
    C. alternative anthropology
    D. ethnology

2. Which of the following is part of the world view of applied anthropology:

    A. attention to small-scale communities
    B. sensitivity to cultural differences
    C. appreciation of alternatives
    D. recognition of systemic complexity
    E. all of the above

3. The growth in the world's population over the past 50 years has primarily been the result of:

    A. higher birth rates
    B. improved health conditions
    C. television
    D. lack of wars
    E. relocation

4. Which of the following is a good reason for North American couples to limit their family size?

    A. each child may cost them as much as half of a million dollars
    B. cultural norms of the majority agree that seven or eight children are too many
    C. children "tie you down"
    D. all of the above

5. Which of the following is **not** a major factor in the decisions of North American couples to limit the number of children they have?

    A. problems of pollution and overpopulation make it irresponsible to have many children
    B. a large family may restrict occupational or spatial mobility
    C. the recreational activities of parents would be restricted by having a large number of children
    D. having large families interferes with women's career goals

6. According to a study by Mahmood Mamdani of a family planning clinic in rural India:

   A. Indian couples did not accept birth control devices
   B. Indian couples though it desirable to have lots of children
   C. villagers of rural India placed a lower cultural value on large families than the staff of the clinic thought
   D. all of the above

7. A restudy of the same rural village in India ten years after Mamdani found:

   A. about half of all couples were either using contraception or were sterilized
   B. couples would rather hire laborers to weed or tend the herds than to have children
   C. the same economic circumstances existed as did before
   D. that couples were desperate to have more sons

8. Families in rural Java:

   A. are paid by the government to use contraception
   B. have their children work for cash to contribute to the family
   C. are economically less successful if they are large
   D. none of the above

9. Which of the following is a reason for high fertility rates in LDCs?

   A. children are no longer valued for their labor
   B. high infant mortality rates encourage having more children
   C. children no longer offer parents economic security in their old age
   D. government-sponsored benefits increase with family size

10. The idea that the major cause of hunger in the Third World is the result of over population of these countries is called:

   A. inequality explanation of hunger
   B. population control explanation of hunger
   C. scarcity explanation of hunger
   D. distribution explanation of hunger

11. Durham's study of hunger in El Salvador showed that:

   A. population growth contributes to hunger by increasing the scarcity of food production resources
   B. small farms produced most of the country's staple foods
   C. large farms are dedicated to the production of export crops
   D. all of the above

12. Indigenous people:

   A. most often survive as ethnic enclaves within a large nation
   B. are sometimes forced to give up their land for the "greater good" of their nation.
   C. are culturally distinct groups that have occupied a region longer than other immigrant or colonist groups.
   D. all of the above

13. In the 19th century, racism and Social Darwinism justified the exploitation of indigenous peoples and their territories. Today:

   A. such exploitation has ceased as a result of international aid
   B. independence and the end of colonial rule has put an end to such exploitation
   C. the same processes are justified in the same way
   D. many similar abuses take place in the name of "development"

14. Indigenous peoples:

   A. are sometimes called "Fourth World" peoples
   B. are sometimes forced to give up their land for the "greater good" of their nation
   C. are culturally distinct "tribal" peoples
   D. all of the above

15. The planting of fruit trees in fallowed fields in parts of Mexico is an example of :

   A. traditional resource management
   B. intercropping
   C. technology transfer
   D. none of the above

16. Idea that it was, or is, the obligation and right of "civilized" peoples to uplift and act in the "best interest" of indigenous people is called:

   A. the Western burden
   B. colonialism
   C. the whiteman's burden
   D. manifest destiny

17. The Central Kalahari Game Reserve:

   A. was set up in 1961 to help the San
   B. excluded the !Kung in the name of conservation
   C. is being destroyed by cattle and vehicles according to the San
   D. all of the above

18.   The Yanomamo:

A. have been successfully assimilated by the Brazilian government
B. have already lost two-thirds of their Brazilian territory
C. built airstrips to attract tourists into their territory
D. helped organize Brazil's National Indian Foundation to control violence against them

19.   Anthropologists are concerned with the rights of indigenous peoples because:

A. they are more aware of what has happened in non-Western cultures in the past several centuries than are most people
B. they identify with indigenous peoples because so many have worked among them
C. they can appreciate the cultures and beliefs of other peoples
D. all of the above

20.   The Kayapo of Brazil:

A. were slaughtered to extinction by ruthless gold miners
B. went extinct from the introduction of new diseases such as influenza and measles
C. are safely protected from the state under the United Nations Charter
D. none of the above

21.   Indigenous peoples are important to pharmaceutical research because:

A. their intimate knowledge of plants and their properties may lead to new discoveries
B. they provide suitable populations for testing new drugs in the field
C. they offer the most lucrative market to drug companies
D. indigenous peoples are not particularly important to pharmaceutical research.

22.   Indigenous peoples are important because:

A. their intimate knowledge of plants and their properties may lead to new discoveries in medicine
B. they have many genetically diverse crops
C. their knowledge of a fish poison helped scientists isolate an important rotenoid
D. all of the above

23.   Which of the following medicines was or were first used by indigenous peoples?

A. willow bark for treating cancer
B. cinchona tree bark for treating malaria
C. periwinkle for pain relief and fever reduction
D. all of the above

24. Preserving the ecological knowledge of indigenous peoples:

    A. is only useful to college professors
    B. is important to pharmaceutical companies
    C. is not important because we already have enough plants for food
    D. is the white man's burden

25. A valuable food grain due to its high protein content but which was prohibited and burned by the Spanish is:

    A. the winged bean of Papua
    B. amaranth
    C. the tepary bean of the American Southwest
    D. the roots of a vine used as fish poison in Southeast Asia

True / False Questions

1. The subfield of applied anthropology has suffered a decline of practitioners over the last decade because of "down-sizing."

2. The highest population growth rate among peoples in the poorest countries is a result of ignorance.

3. To many poor families, children are seen as an economic asset and not a liability.

4. In the last fifty years world population has doubled, jumping from 2.5 billion to more than 6 billion.

5. Middle-income parents can anticipate paying around $150,000 for their child's expenses.

6. Rural families in LDCs don't seem to understand that children are an economic liability.

7. Studies of a rural Indian village by Mamdani, Nag, and Kak found that couples have more children even when the economic costs of large families outweigh their benefits.

8. One reasons rural families in the LDCs have many children is the high rate of infant mortality.

9. The argument that the unequal distribution of resources is responsible for chronic hunger for most of the world's people is called the scarcity explanation of hunger.

10. In their books *Food First* and *World Hunger: Twelve Myths*, Lappe and Collins claim that every nation could provide an adequate diet for its citizens if its productive resources were equitably distributed.

11. The global economy has resulted in the increasing use of land in Third World countries for the production of export crops instead of food for the local population.

12. In his sturdy of hunger and poverty in El Salvador, Durham noted that population growth was only part of the reason for the hunger of El Salvador's rural poor.

13. Traditional agricultural systems are surprisingly much more efficient in terms of energy than modern mechanized agriculture.

14. Intercropping has been practiced for centuries by shifting cultivators.

15. Brazil arrested several indigenous Kayapo leaders as "foreigners" engaging in political activity harmful to the nation when they protested the building of dams on their native lands.

16. The Madagascar periwinkle has long been used in folk medicine to treat digestive ailments.

17. About one-fourth of all prescribed drugs in the U.S. contain active ingredients extracted from plants.

18. Over the course of human history, several thousand species of plants have been use for food and most of these have been domesticated.

19. High protein plants such as quinoa and amaranth are eaten by Mesoamericans and South Americans.

20. If the tropical forests and the cultural knowledge of their indigenous inhabitants last long enough, additional plants with medical value will probably be discovered.

Multiple Choice Answers

1.	A	(p. 374)
2.	E	(p. 374)
3.	B	(p. 375)
4.	D	(p. 376)
5.	A	(p. 376)
6.	B	(p. 377)
7.	A	(p. 377)
8.	D	(p. 378)
9.	B	(p. 378)
10.	C	(p. 379)
11.	D	(p. 380-381)
12.	D	(p. 384)
13.	D	(p. 384-385)

14.	D	(p. 384)
15.	A	(p. 384)
16.	C	(p. 385)
17.	C	(p. 386)
18.	B	(p. 385-386)
19.	D	(p. 387-388)
20.	D	(p. 387)
21.	A	(p. 388-389)
22.	D	(p. 388-390)
23.	B	(p. 388-389)
24.	B	(p. 389)
25.	B	(p. 390)

True / False Answers

1.	F	(p. 374)
2.	F	(p. 375)
3.	T	(p. 375)
4.	T	(p. 375)
5.	F	(p. 375)
6.	F	(p. 376-378)
7.	F	(p. 377)
8.	T	(p. 377-378)
9.	F	(p. 379)
10.	T	(p. 380)

11.	T	(p. 381)
12.	T	(p. 380-381)
13.	T	(p. 382)
14.	T	(p. 383)
15.	T	(p. 387)
16.	F	(p. 388)
17.	T	(p. 389)
18.	F	(p. 389)
19.	T	(p. 390)
20.	T	(p. 390)